WATERHAMMER ANALYSIS

by

JOHN PARMAKIAN

Assistant Chief Designing Engineer
Bureau of Reclamation
Denver, Colorado

DOVER PUBLICATIONS, INC.

New York

Published in Canada by General Publishing Company, Ltd., 30 Lesmill Road, Don Mills, Toronto, Ontario.
Published in the United Kingdom by Constable and Company, Ltd., 10 Orange Street, London WC 2.

This Dover edition, first published in 1963, is an unabridged and corrected republication of the work first published by Prentice-Hall, Inc., in 1955.

International Standard Book Number: 0-486-61061-6

Library of Congress Catalog Card Number: 63-19498

Manufactured in the United States of America
Dover Publications, Inc.
180 Varick Street
New York, N. Y. 10014

to Del

Preface to First Edition

This book is the result of a gradual development originating from a course of instruction for graduate and undergraduate engineering students at the University of Colorado. However, in addition to the requirements of class instruction, an attempt is made to meet the needs of the engineer who is primarily interested in the solution of practical waterhammer problems. It is hoped that this work will serve as a stimulus to the further study of some phases of waterhammer analysis in which our knowledge is still somewhat fragmentary.

It is understandable that a book on this subject must, for the most part, be an adaptation of material drawn from many sources. A partial list of references to such literature is given at the end of the text. The reader will also find a considerable amount of material that is either new or which has not previously been presented in the convenient form given here. The treatment of the subject is systematic, and the results of many important types of analyses are presented in graph form to facilitate the solution of similar waterhammer problems without recourse to detailed procedures.

This material has been used during the past ten years to analyze the waterhammer phenomena at major hydraulic structures which have been designed and built by the Bureau of Reclamation. Sufficient field test data have been obtained at these structures to demonstrate the reliability of the methods of analysis described in the text.

For a proper understanding of this book an elementary knowledge of hydraulics and calculus is considered essential. For a complete course of study the reader is urged to solve the problems at the end of the book. These problems have been carefully selected to illustrate and supplement the text material.

To a great extent the publication of this work was made possible by the willingness of the following major hydraulic turbine manufacturers to defray part of the cost of publication:

ALLIS-CHALMERS MANUFACTURING COMPANY
BALDWIN-LIMA-HAMILTON CORPORATION
THE JAMES LEFFEL & COMPANY
NEWPORT NEWS SHIPBUILDING AND DRY DOCK COMPANY
S. MORGAN SMITH COMPANY

In this connection I am especially indebted to G. Dugan Johnson, Chief Hydraulic Engineer of S. Morgan Smith Company, for initiating and obtaining this cooperative assistance.

Much valuable assistance was given by my past and present colleagues at the Bureau of Reclamation. Of these I wish to thank F. E. Cornwell, C. C. Crawford, and W. E. Evans, whose suggestions have influenced much of the text material. The illustrations were prepared by R. H. Williams. The solutions of the waterhammer problems at the end of the book were worked out independently by Benjamin Donsky and C. W. Lundgren. The assistance of Mr. Donsky and F. O. Ruud in proofreading the text and illustrations is also acknowledged. Finally, I wish to thank L. N. McClellan, Assistant Commissioner and Chief Engineer of the Bureau of Reclamation, and Professor Warren Raeder, Head of the Department of Civil Engineering at the University of Colorado, for the privilege and opportunity to teach the first course of study on this subject at the University.

JOHN PARMAKIAN

Denver, Colorado
1955

Preface to Dover Edition

The Dover edition of *Waterhammer Analysis* is the same as the original edition with the exception that several subscript errors and missing decimal points in a few of the figures have been corrected. To date no important exceptions to the material contained in the book have come to the author's attention.

JOHN PARMAKIAN

Denver, Colorado
1963

Contents

Notation

Description	Symbol	Units

1. *Conduit Dimensions and General Symbols*

Description	Symbol	Units
Cross-sectional area of pipe or conduit	A	ft^2
Thickness of pipe wall	e	ft
Inside diameter of conduit	D	ft
Inside radius of conduit	R	ft
Modulus of elasticity of pipe wall material	E	lb/ft^2
Modulus of rigidity of tunnel material	G	lb/ft^2
Acceleration of gravity	g	ft/sec^2
Bulk modulus of water	K	lb/ft^2
Total length of conduit	L	ft
Length of any uniform section of conduit	L_n	ft
Specific weight of water	w	lb/ft^3
Distance measured positive from lower end to point on conduit	x	ft
Distance measured in opposite direction from x	x_1	ft
Height of point on conduit measured above center line of control gate	Z	ft
Angle of slope of conduit	α	—
Poisson's ratio for the pipe wall material	μ	—
Longitudinal stress in pipe wall	σ_1	lb/ft^2
Circumferential stress in pipe wall	σ_2	lb/ft^2

2. *Pressure and Head Symbols for Gate Operation*

Description	Symbol	Units
Pressure head for steady conditions (when gate is submerged, H_0 is taken as the net head on gate)	H_0	ft
Pressure head for surge conditions	H	ft
Pressure rise above normal	H_a	ft
Pressure drop below normal	H_a'	ft
Ratio H/H_0	h	—
Friction head	H_f	ft
Ratio H_f/H_0	h_f	
Unit pressure	P	lb/ft^2

Description	Symbol	Units
3. *Velocity and Time Symbols*		
Velocity of pressure wave	a	ft/sec
Round trip wave travel time	$2L/a$	sec
Number of $2L/a$ time intervals	N	—
Initial steady flow in conduit	Q_0	ft³/sec
Time	t	sec
Time of gate travel	T	sec
Velocity in conduit for initial steady conditions	V_0	ft/sec
Velocity in conduit for final steady conditions	V_e	ft/sec
Velocity in conduit for surge conditions	V	ft/sec
Velocity ratio V/V_0 or V/V_e	v	—
Difference between initial and final steady velocities	V'	ft/sec
4. *Waterhammer Symbols*		
Pressure wave travelling in direction of $+x$	F	ft
Pressure wave travelling in direction of $-x$	f	ft
Pipe line constant	ρ	—
Reflection factor	r	—
Transmission factor	s	—
5. *Gate-Opening Symbols*		
Cross-sectional area through gate opening	A_g	ft²
Gate opening factor as defined by equation (28)	B	ft^{1/2}/sec
Coefficient of discharge through gate	C_d	—
Effective discharge area of gate	$C_d A_g$	ft²
Proportion of full gate effective opening	τ	—
6. *Pump Operation Symbols*		
Ratio of pump speed at any time to rated pump speed	α	—
Ratio of pump input torque at any time to pump input torque at rated speed and head	β	—
Pressure head for surge conditions measured above the pump intake water surface elevation	H	ft

Description	Symbol	Units
Pumping head for initial steady pumping conditions	H_0	ft
Rated pumping head	H_R	ft
Friction head	H_f	ft
Ratio of pressure head for surge conditions to rated pumping head; $h = H/H_R$	h	—
Ratio of friction head to rated pumping head	h_f	—
Defined by equation (50)	K_1	sec^{-1}
Pump input torque	M	lb ft
Pump speed	N	rpm
Pump efficiency at rated speed and head	η	—
Angular velocity of pump and motor shaft	ω	rad/sec
Flywheel effect of rotating parts of motor, pump and entrained water	WR^2	lb ft^2
Mass moment of inertia of rotating parts	I	lb ft sec^2

7. *Surge Tank Symbols*

Description	Symbol	Units
Cross-sectional area of pipe	A	ft^2
Cross-sectional area of surge tank orifice	A_2	ft^2
Dimensionless parameter	b	—
Cross-sectional area of surge tank	F	ft^2
Accelerating head on water column	H_a	ft
Hydraulic losses in pipe line	H_{f1}	ft
Surge tank throttling loss	H_{f2}	ft
Length of pipe line between reservoir and surge tank	L	ft
Initial flow through turbine or pump	Q_0	ft^3/sec
Final flow through turbine or pump	Q_e	ft^3/sec
Displacement of water level in surge tank measured positive above static level	S	ft
Maximum displacement of water level in surge tank measured from operating level due to instantaneous stopping of flow Q_0	S_A	ft
Maximum displacement of water level in surge tank measured from static level due to instantaneous starting of flow Q_e	S_B	ft
Function of S	S_2	—
Time	t	sec
Function of t	t_1	—

Description	Symbol	Units
Time at maximum upsurge	T	sec
Velocity in penstock between reservoir and surge tank	V_1	ft/sec

8. *Air Chamber Symbols*

Description	Symbol	Units
Cross-sectional area of pump discharge line	A	ft^2
Volume of compressed air in air chamber	C	ft^3
Ratio of volume of compressed air in air chamber at any time to initial volume, $c = C/C_0$	c	—
Total volume of air chamber (compressed air and water)	C'	ft^3
Pressure head at air chamber referred to absolute zero	H^*	ft
Ratio of absolute pressure head at air chamber at any time to initial pressure head, $h^* = H^*/H_0^*$	h^*	—
Coefficient of head loss such that KH_0^* is the total head loss for a flow of Q_0 into air chamber	K	—
Length of pump discharge line	L	ft
Velocity of flow in the pump discharge line	V	ft/sec
Initial flow through pump	Q_0	ft^3/sec
Pipe line characteristic as defined by equation (76)	ρ^*	—
Air chamber characteristic	$2C_0a/Q_0L$	—

9. *Subscripts*

Description	Symbol	Units
Subscripts $1, 2, 3 \ldots n$; designation of time in seconds when applied to H, h, V, v, B, etc. Refers also to physical pipe-line section dimensions A, a, L, D, etc.	sub (n)	—
Subscript 0 refers to initial steady values at $t = 0$ prior to surge conditions	sub (0)	—
Subscript e refers to final steady values following surge conditions	sub (e)	—
Subscript R as applied to pump operation symbols refers to rated values at rated speed and head	sub (R)	—

I

Rigid Water Column Theory

1. Basic equations[1]

When a closed pipe is filled with moving water, the laws governing the changes of pressure and discharge depend upon the conditions under which the flow occurs. If the water is considered to be incompressible and the velocity of water which passes through any section of the pipe remains constant, Bernoulli's

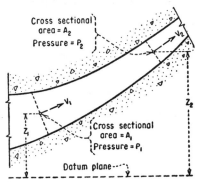

Cross sectional area = A_2
Pressure = P_2

V_2

V_1

Z_2

Cross sectional area = A_1
Pressure = P_1

Datum plane

Bernoulli's equation for steady frictionless flow:

$$\frac{P_1}{w} + Z_1 + \frac{V_1^2}{2g} = \frac{P_2}{w} + Z_2 + \frac{V_2^2}{2g} = \text{Constant}$$

Figure 1

energy equation applies at any two sections of the pipe as shown in Figure 1. However, when the motion is unsteady, that is, when the discharge at each section is varying rapidly from one instant to the next, rapid pressure changes occur inside the pipe and the Bernoulli equation is no longer applicable. Such pressure changes are referred to as "waterhammer" because of the hammering sound which often accompanies the phenomena.

[1] See Reference 4.

1

In order to obtain the basic physical laws of waterhammer, the effect of rapid changes in flow are first considered for a pipe line of uniform area A and length L as shown in Figure 2. The pipe line is connected to a reservoir at its upper end and has a control gate at the lower end for regulating the discharge of water into the atmosphere. Since it is desired to present the theory initially in its simplest form, it is assumed that

(a) The water in the pipe is incompressible.

(b) The pipe walls do not stretch regardless of the pressure inside the pipe.

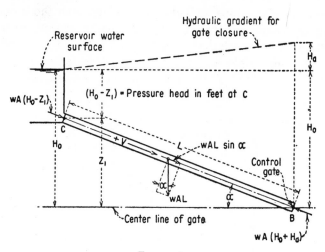

Figure 2

(c) The pipe line remains full of water at all times and the minimum pressure inside the pipe is in excess of the vapor pressure of water.

(d) The hydraulic losses and velocity head are negligible when compared with the pressure changes.

(e) The velocity of water in the direction of the axis of the pipe is uniform over any cross section of the pipe.

(f) The pressure is uniform over a transverse cross section of the pipe and is equal to the pressure at the center line of the pipe.

(g) The reservoir level remains constant during the gate-movement time.

If the flow at the control gate is altered, an unbalanced external force will act at the gate on the mass of the water column. The magnitude of this unbalanced force is now determined using Newton's second law of motion. The deceleration, or the rate at which the velocity decreases per unit of time, is $-dV/dt$, where V is measured positive in the direction of flow. The mass of water decelerated in the entire length of the pipe line is wAL/g. If H_a designates the decelerating head or head rise at the gate, the unbalanced force acting on the water column is

$$wA[(H_0 + H_a) - (H_0 - Z_1) - L \sin \alpha],$$

but since $L \sin \alpha = Z_1$, the resulting unbalanced force on the column of water is wAH_a.[2]

Then from Newton's second law of motion,

$$H_a = -\frac{L}{g}\frac{dV}{dt}. \tag{1}$$

Prior to a closing movement of the control gate, the discharge into the atmosphere is

$$Q_0 = AV_0 = (C_d A_g)_0 \sqrt{2gH_0},$$

or

$$V_0 = B_0\sqrt{H_0},$$

where

$$B_0 = \frac{(C_d A_g)_0 \sqrt{2g}}{A}.$$

Then at any instant during the gate movement,

$$V = B\sqrt{H_0 + H_a},$$

and

$$\frac{V}{V_0} = \frac{B}{B_0}\sqrt{1 + \frac{H_a}{H_0}}.$$

If the ratio B/B_0 is designated τ,

$$V = \tau V_0\sqrt{1 + \frac{H_a}{H_0}}, \tag{2}$$

where τ is a function of time which defines the ratio of the effective gate opening at any time during the gate closure to the ef-

---

[2] Note that the slope of the pipe does not appear in the final expression for the unbalanced force. In general, for a pipe line of variable slope, the distance $Z_1 = \int_0^L (\sin \alpha)\, dL$, from which the unbalanced force is always wAH_a. The analysis is therefore valid for a horizontal pipe or a pipe line with any type of profile.

fective gate opening at time zero. Equations (1) and (2) are the basic waterhammer equations for gate closure as defined by the rigid water column theory.

2. Uniform gate operation

For a partial or complete uniform gate closure

$$\tau = 1 - \frac{V't}{V_0 T} \qquad (0 \leqq t \leqq T),$$

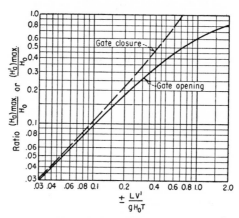

g = acceleration of gravity in feet per second²
(H_0) max. = maximum rise in head in feet at the gate
due to gate closure.
(H_0') max. = maximum drop in head in feet at the gate
due to gate opening.
H_0 = Initial steady head at the gate in feet.
L = Length of pipe in feet.
T = Time for gate closure or opening in seconds.
V' = Difference between initial and final steady
velocities in feet per second.

WATERHAMMER FOR UNIFORM GATE
OPERATION – RIGID WATER COLUMN THEORY

Figure 3

where T is the gate movement time and V' is the difference between the initial steady water velocity and the final steady velocity of water in the pipe. Then

$$V = \left(V_0 - \frac{V't}{T}\right) \sqrt{1 + \frac{H_a}{H_0}}. \qquad (3)$$

Equations (1) and (3) are now solved simultaneously for

$$(H_a)_{\max},$$

the maximum head rise at the gate, by setting dH_a/dt equal to zero. Then

$$\frac{(H_a)_{\max}}{H_0} = \frac{K_1}{2} + \sqrt{K_1 + \frac{K_1^2}{4}}, \qquad (4)$$

where
$$K_1 = \left(\frac{LV'}{gH_0T}\right)^2.$$

A similar procedure for determining

$$(H_a')_{\max},$$

the maximum head drop at the gate due to a uniform gate opening, results in the equation

$$\frac{(H_a')_{\max}}{H_0} = \frac{K_1}{2} - \sqrt{K_1 + \frac{K_1^2}{4}}. \qquad (5)$$

The solution of Equations (4) and (5) for uniform gate operation is obtained readily from Figure 3.

3. Example

Consider the pipe line shown in Figure 4. At this installation the initial flow of 1500 cubic feet per second is reduced to 500 cubic feet per second by a uniform gate closure in 12 seconds. Then

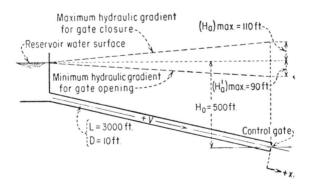

Figure 4

$$\frac{LV'}{gH_0T} = 0.20 \quad \text{and} \quad \frac{(H_a)_{\text{max}}}{H_0} = 0.22,$$

from which the maximum head rise at the gate is 110 feet. If the control gate is opened uniformly in 12 seconds to increase the flow by 1000 cubic feet per second, $(H_a')_{\text{max}}$ is 90 feet and the minimum head at the gate is 410 feet. Since the head changes along the pipe line are proportional to the length measured along the pipe from the reservoir end, the maximum and minimum hydraulic gradients vary along the length of the line as shown in Figure 4.

4. Equivalent length of pipe line

Consider a pipe line with one stepwise change in the diameter as shown in Figure 5. If the effects of the hydraulic losses and velocity head are neglected, the forces acting on the ends of the two water columns correspond to those shown in the figure. The

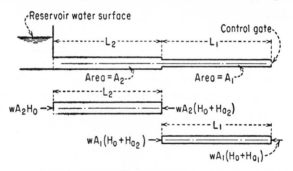

Figure 5

following relations for the dynamic equilibrium of the two water columns are then applicable:

$$wA_1(H_{a_1} - H_{a_2}) = -\frac{w}{g}A_1L_1\frac{dV_1}{dt};$$

$$wA_2H_{a_2} = -\frac{w}{g}A_2L_2\frac{dV_2}{dt},$$

where V_1 and V_2 are the water velocities in the pipe lengths L_1 and L_2, respectively. From the condition of continuity $A_1V_1 = A_2V_2$. The solution of these equations for H_{a_1} is

$$H_{a_1} = -\frac{A_1}{g}\left(\frac{L_1}{A_1} + \frac{L_2}{A_2}\right)\frac{dV_1}{dt}.$$

This equation is similar in form to Equation (1) if L is replaced by the term $L_1 + \frac{L_2 A_1}{A_2}$. Hence a pipe line with one stepwise change in the diameter is replaced, for the purposes of waterhammer by an equivalent uniform pipe line of area A_1 and length L, where

$$L = L_1 + \frac{L_2 A_1}{A_2}.$$

Although only one stepwise change in area is considered here, a similar procedure applies for a pipe line consisting of any number of stepwise changes in the diameter. That is, a pipe line consisting of a number of pipe sections of lengths L_n and areas A_n is replaced for waterhammer purposes by an equivalent uniform pipe line of length L and area A_1, by making the substitution

$$L = L_1 + \frac{L_2 A_1}{A_2} + \frac{L_3 A_1}{A_3} + \ldots + \frac{L_n A_1}{A_n}, \tag{6}$$

where L_1 is the actual length of the pipe section whose area is A_1, and L_2 is the actual length of the pipe section whose area is A_2, etc.

5. Limitations of theory

The rigid water column theory assumes that the pipe walls are rigid and the water is incompressible. Consequently, pressure changes at the gate are felt immediately throughout the pipe. For relatively slow gate movements this theory provides a simple means for determining the waterhammer effects. For example, for uniform gate operation, Figure 3 gives satisfactory results only when T is greater than about $L/1000$. For rapid gate movements the elastic water column theory which is described in the following chapters must be used.

II

Elastic Water Column Theory

6. Basic considerations[1]

Fundamental waterhammer equations are now derived for a more general case of variable flow. The same assumptions used in the preceding chapter are applicable with the exception that the elasticity of the pipe walls and the compressibility of the water under the action of a pressure change are also taken into account. An element of water which is bounded by two parallel faces normal to the axis of the pipe is considered. The condition of dynamic equilibrium requires that the unbalanced force acting on the element of water be made equal to the product of the element's mass and acceleration; that is, Newton's second law of motion is satisfied. The condition of continuity for the element requires that all available space inside the boundaries of the element be occupied by water at all times. The equations resulting from the conditions of dynamic equilibrium and continuity are then solved simultaneously to obtain the fundamental waterhammer equations.[2]

7. Condition of dynamic equilibrium

The condition of dynamic equilibrium for an element of water dx_1 in length is set up as follows by referring to Figure 6. In passing from the face B to the face C, the cross-sectional area of the pipe increases at a rate of $\partial A / \partial x_1$. If the area at B is defined as A, the area at C is then $A + \dfrac{\partial A}{\partial x_1} dx_1$. The pressure intensity

---

[1] See Reference 47.

[2] A simplified derivation of the fundamental waterhammer equations is possible by assuming that the wave transmission phenomena are known to exist inside the pipe as described in Reference 32. In the analysis presented here, the derivation is obtained from more basic considerations.

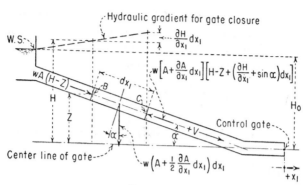

Figure 6

and the total forces acting on the faces B and C are then determined in a similar manner, and are shown in the following tabulation:

Location	Face B	Face C
Area	A	$A + \dfrac{\partial A}{\partial x_1} dx_1$
Pressure	$w(H - Z)$	$w\left[H - Z + \left(\dfrac{\partial H}{\partial x_1} + \sin \alpha \right) dx_1 \right]$
Force	$wA(H - Z)$	$w\left(A + \dfrac{\partial A}{\partial x_1} dx_1 \right)\left[H - Z + \left(\dfrac{\partial H}{\partial x_1} + \sin \alpha \right) dx_1 \right]$

At the center of gravity of the element, the force of gravity acting vertically downward on the mass of the element is

$$w\left(A + \frac{1}{2} \frac{\partial A}{\partial x_1} dx_1 \right) dx_1.$$

The unbalanced decelerating force acting along the axis of the pipe is then

$$w\left(A + \frac{\partial A}{\partial x_1} dx_1 \right)\left[H - Z + \left(\frac{\partial H}{\partial x_1} + \sin \alpha \right) dx_1 \right]$$

$$-wA(H - Z) - w\left(A + \frac{1}{2} \frac{\partial A}{\partial x_1} dx_1 \right) dx_1 \sin \alpha,$$

where the positive direction of the force is taken opposite to the direction of the normal flow. After neglecting terms of higher order and cancelling like terms, the unbalanced decelerating force acting along the axis of the pipe reduces to

$$w\left[A\,\frac{\partial H}{\partial x_1} + (H - Z)\,\frac{\partial A}{\partial x_1}\right]dx_1.$$

It may be shown that $w(H - Z)\,\dfrac{\partial A}{\partial x_1}\,dx_1$ is always very small when compared with $wA\,\dfrac{\partial H}{\partial x_1}\,dx_1$, and the unbalanced decelerating force acting along the axis of the pipe reduces to $wA\,\dfrac{\partial H}{\partial x_1}\,dx_1$.

The mass of the element of water to be moved is $wA\,dx_1/g$ and its deceleration is $-dV/dt$. Then from Newton's second law of motion

$$-wA\,\frac{\partial H}{\partial x_1}\,dx_1 = \frac{wA}{g}\,\frac{dV}{dt}\,dx_1.$$

Since V is a function of both x_1 and t,

$$\frac{dV}{dt} = \frac{\partial V}{\partial t} + \frac{\partial V}{\partial x_1}\frac{dx_1}{dt} = \frac{\partial V}{\partial t} + V\frac{\partial V}{\partial x_1}.$$

Then
$$\frac{\partial H}{\partial x_1} = -\frac{1}{g}\left(\frac{\partial V}{\partial t} + V\,\frac{\partial V}{\partial x_1}\right), \tag{7}$$

which is the equation of equilibrium for the element of water.

8. Condition of continuity

A second equation relating H and V is now determined from the condition of continuity. Figure 7a shows an element of water of length BC equal to dx_1 at any time t. For a given instant of time the rate of change of velocity between the faces B and C of the element is $\partial V/\partial x_1$ and the velocities at B and C are V and $V + \dfrac{\partial V}{\partial x_1}\,dx_1$, respectively. In Figure 7b a very short time interval of dt seconds has elapsed, and the element of water BC has moved to DF. Since V is a function of two independent variables x_1 and t, the velocities at the two faces D and F are determined to be as shown in Figure 7b. The change in length of the element

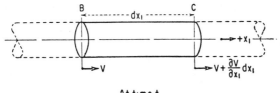

At time t

(a)

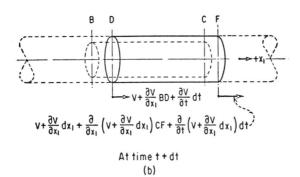

At time $t + dt$

(b)

Figure 7

dx_1 in moving from BC to DF is $BD - CF$. The average velocity of the face B in moving to D during the time interval dt is

$$V + \frac{1}{2} \frac{\partial V}{\partial x_1} BD + \frac{1}{2} \frac{\partial V}{\partial t} dt,$$

and the distance moved during the time interval dt is BD. Then

$$BD = \left(V + \frac{1}{2} \frac{\partial V}{\partial x_1} BD + \frac{1}{2} \frac{\partial V}{\partial t} dt \right) dt.$$

Similarly,

$$CF = \left[V + \frac{\partial V}{\partial x_1} dx_1 + \frac{1}{2} \frac{\partial}{\partial x_1} \left(V + \frac{\partial V}{\partial x_1} dx_1 \right) CF \right.$$
$$\left. + \frac{1}{2} \frac{\partial}{\partial t} \left(V + \frac{\partial V}{\partial x_1} dx_1 \right) dt \right] dt.$$

Then, after neglecting terms of higher order,

$$BD - CF = -\frac{\partial V}{\partial x_1} dx_1 \, dt. \tag{8}$$

The change in length of the element dx_1 is effected primarily by two factors. In the first place, a change in pressure causes the pipe shell to expand or contract. The resulting change in the cross-sectional area then produces a change in the length of the element in order to contain the same volume of water. In the second place, because of the compressibility of water, a change in pressure causes a change in the volume of water within the element, and as a consequence, a further change in the length of the element. The total change in the length of the element, that is, $BD - CF$ is now computed by considering the elasticity of both the pipe shell and the water.

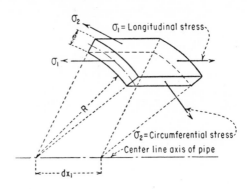

σ_1 = Axial or longitudinal stress in pipe shell.

σ_2 = Hoop or circumferential stress in pipe shell.

Figure 8

Referring to Figure 8, the deformation of the element[3] of the pipe shell produced by a change in the longitudinal and circumferential stresses is

$$\Delta R = \frac{R + e/2}{E} \left(\Delta\sigma_2 - \mu\Delta\sigma_1 \right)$$

$$\cong \frac{R}{E} \left(\Delta\sigma_2 - \mu\Delta\sigma_1 \right),$$

and the change in the axial length of the element is

$$\delta x_1 = \frac{dx_1}{E} \left(\Delta\sigma_1 - \mu\Delta\sigma_2 \right),$$

where $\Delta\sigma_1$ and $\Delta\sigma_2$ represent the change in the longitudinal and circumferential stresses, respectively, produced by a change in

[3] See Reference 45.

pressure. The volume enclosed by the newly stressed element is $\pi(R + \Delta R)^2 (\delta x_1 + dx_1)$ and the change in length of the original element BC compatible with the change in volume is

$$\frac{\pi(R + \Delta R)^2 (\delta x_1 + dx_1) - \pi R^2 dx_1}{\pi R^2}.$$

After neglecting terms which are very small when compared with those retained, the total change in length of the element is found to be

$$\delta x_1 + \frac{2 \Delta R}{R} dx_1.$$

The change in the longitudinal stress is dependent upon the ability of the pipe to move in a longitudinal direction. Several typical cases are considered in which the movement of the pipe is restricted to varying extents:

(a) For a pipe anchored at the upper end, free to move in a longitudinal direction throughout its length, and without expansion joints, the longitudinal and circumferential stresses produced by a pressure change of $w\,dH$ are

$$\Delta\sigma_1 = \frac{wD\,dH}{4e}; \qquad \Delta\sigma_2 = \frac{wD\,dH}{2e}.$$

Then the total change in length is

$$\begin{aligned}
\delta x_1 + \frac{2 \Delta R}{R} dx_1 &= \frac{dx_1}{E}\left(\frac{wD\,dH}{4e} - \frac{\mu wD\,dH}{2e}\right) \\
&\quad + \frac{2\,dx_1}{E}\left(\frac{wD\,dH}{2e} - \frac{\mu wD\,dH}{4e}\right) \\
&= \frac{wD\,dH}{Ee}\left(\frac{5}{4} - \mu\right) dx_1.
\end{aligned}$$

(b) For a pipe which is anchored against longitudinal movement throughout its length

$$\Delta\sigma_1 = \frac{\mu wD\,dH}{2e}; \qquad \Delta\sigma_2 = \frac{wD\,dH}{2e};$$

from which

$$\delta x_1 + \frac{2 \Delta R}{R} dx_1 = \frac{wD\,dH}{Ee}(1 - \mu^2)\,dx_1.$$

(c) For a pipe which has expansion joints between anchors throughout the length of the pipe

$$\Delta\sigma_1 = 0; \qquad \Delta\sigma_2 = \frac{wD\,dH}{2e};$$

from which

$$\delta x_1 + \frac{2\,\Delta R}{R}\,dx_1 = \frac{wD\,dH}{Ee}\left(1 - \frac{\mu}{2}\right)dx_1.$$

The total change in length of the element produced by a pressure change of $w\,dH$ for the three cases listed above is then

$$\delta x_1 + \frac{2\,\Delta R}{R}\,dx_1 = \frac{wD\,dH\,dx_1}{Ee}\,c_1,$$

where for case

(a) $c_1 = \dfrac{5}{4} - \mu,$

(b) $c_1 = 1 - \mu^2,$

(c) $c_1 = 1 - \dfrac{\mu}{2}.$

The change in volume of the original element of water, dx_1 in length, because of the elasticity of water under the action of a pressure change $w\,dH$, is

$$\frac{w\pi R^2}{K}\,dH\,dx_1,$$

and the corresponding change in length of the element of water is

$$\frac{w\pi R^2}{K\pi R^2}\,dH\,dx_1 = \frac{w}{K}\,dH\,dx_1.$$

The total change in length of the element of water caused by a pressure change $w\,dH$, when both the compressibility of the water and the deformation of the pipe are considered, reduces to

$$w\left(\frac{1}{K} + \frac{Dc_1}{Ee}\right)dH\,dx_1.$$

Since H is a function of x_1 and t, and $dx_1/dt = V$, it follows that

$$dH = \frac{\partial H}{\partial t}\,dt + \frac{\partial H}{\partial x_1}\,dx_1 = \left(\frac{\partial H}{\partial t} + V\frac{\partial H}{\partial x_1}\right)dt.$$

The total change in length of the element produced by a pressure change as defined by Equation (8) is then

$$BD - CF = -\frac{\partial V}{\partial x_1} dx_1 \, dt$$

$$= w\left(\frac{1}{K} + \frac{Dc_1}{Ee}\right)\left(\frac{\partial H}{\partial t} + V \frac{\partial H}{\partial x_1}\right) dx_1 \, dt.$$

Then

$$\frac{\partial V}{\partial x_1} = -w\left(\frac{1}{K} + \frac{Dc_1}{Ee}\right)\left(\frac{\partial H}{\partial t} + V \frac{\partial H}{\partial x_1}\right),$$

or

$$\frac{\partial H}{\partial t} + V \frac{\partial H}{\partial x_1} = -\frac{a^2}{g} \cdot \frac{\partial V}{\partial x_1}, \tag{9}$$

where

$$a = \sqrt{\frac{1}{\dfrac{w}{g}\left(\dfrac{1}{K} + \dfrac{Dc_1}{Ee}\right)}}. \tag{10}$$

9. Fundamental waterhammer equations

Equations (7) and (9) are now solved simultaneously. It is initially assumed in Equation (7) that the term $V \dfrac{\partial V}{\partial x_1}$ is small when compared with $\partial V/\partial t$, and in Equation (9) the term $V \dfrac{\partial H}{\partial x_1}$ is small when compared with $\partial H/\partial t$. Before the final solution which results from these assumptions is accepted, their validity will be verified. Equations (7) and (9) are then rewritten in the following form:

$$\frac{\partial H}{\partial x_1} = -\frac{1}{g} \frac{\partial V}{\partial t}; \tag{11}$$

$$\frac{\partial H}{\partial t} = -\frac{a^2}{g} \frac{\partial V}{\partial x_1}. \tag{12}$$

The general solutions of these equations are

$$H - H_0 = f\left(t - \frac{x_1}{a}\right) + F\left(t + \frac{x_1}{a}\right); \tag{13}$$

$$V - V_0 = \frac{g}{a}\left[f\left(t - \frac{x_1}{a}\right) - F\left(t + \frac{x_1}{a}\right)\right]. \tag{14}$$

For the sake of simplifying the mathematical derivations of the fundamental waterhammer equations, it was found convenient to express x_1 and V as positive when they were both measured in the same direction, that is, from the reservoir to the gate. However, in the solution of waterhammer problems involving a gate movement at the lower end it is more convenient to express the distance to a section of the pipe from the lower end of the pipe as a positive distance, since the initial disturbance in the flow occurs first at the lower end of the pipe and then moves up the pipe. Equations (13) and (14) are then written in the following form, where $-x = x_1$:

$$H - H_0 = F\left(t - \frac{x}{a}\right) + f\left(t + \frac{x}{a}\right); \tag{15}$$

$$V - V_0 = -\frac{g}{a}\left[F\left(t - \frac{x}{a}\right) - f\left(t + \frac{x}{a}\right)\right]. \tag{16}$$

These equations are the fundamental equations of waterhammer. In these equations the positive directions of the velocities are in the direction of decreasing values of x.

10. Physical significance of waterhammer equations

From an examination of Equation (15) it is seen that, dimensionally, $F\left(t - \frac{x}{a}\right)$ is a pressure height which is measured in the same units as H, that is, in feet of water. For a definite instant of

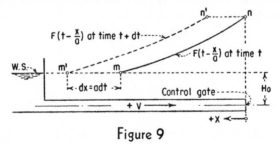

Figure 9

time, $F\left(t - \frac{x}{a}\right)$ is a function of x only, and can be represented by a certain curve such as mn in Figure 9. After a small interval of time dt has passed, the argument of the function F becomes $t + dt - \frac{x + dx}{a}$. However, the magnitude of the function F is unchanged provided that, with an increase of t by dt, the abscissa is increased by an amount dx equal to $a\,dt$, from which $x = at +$ a constant. This means that the curve mn which is constructed for the instant of time designated as t can also be used for the instant of time $t + dt$, provided that it is displaced in the direction of positive x by the distance $dx = a\,dt$ as shown by the dotted line $m'n'$. Hence the function $F\left(t - \dfrac{x}{a}\right)$ represents a pressure wave which moves in the direction of positive x with a velocity of a feet per second. A similar explanation can be used to explain the physical significance of the function $f\left(t + \dfrac{x}{a}\right)$ by letting $x = -at +$ a constant. This term represents a pressure wave which moves in the direction of negative x with a velocity of a feet per second as shown in Figure 10.

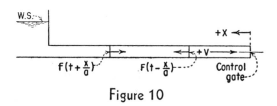

Figure 10

The significance of Equations (15) and (16) is now clear. Equation (15) implies that at time t at a point in the pipe with coordinate x, the head rise is equal to the sum of the traveling pressure heights or waves comprising F and f.[4] These waves are propagated in opposite directions in the pipe with a constant velocity of a feet per second. When an F wave passes an f wave, neither wave is attenuated or undergoes a change in shape. Equation (16) is a relation between the magnitude of the pressure heights F and f and the change in velocity which occurs at a section of the moving column of water.

Before the fundamental waterhammer equations are accepted as a valid approximation of the conditions which exist in the pipe, it must be shown that $V\dfrac{\partial V}{\partial x_1} = -V\dfrac{\partial V}{\partial x}$ is small when compared

---

[4] The terms F and f are used as abbreviations to represent

$$F\left(t - \frac{x}{a}\right) \quad \text{and} \quad f\left(t + \frac{x}{a}\right).$$

with $\partial V/\partial t$; and that $V\dfrac{\partial H}{\partial x_1} = -V\dfrac{\partial H}{\partial x}$ is small when compared with $\partial H/\partial t$, as these assumptions were made in deriving the equations. In the physical interpretation of the terms $F\left(t - \dfrac{x}{a}\right)$ and $f\left(t + \dfrac{x}{a}\right)$ it was shown that these terms represent pressure functions which move inside the pipe in the direction of $+x$ and $-x$, respectively, with a velocity of a feet per second. Furthermore, it was shown that there is a definite relation between the variables x and t, namely that $x = \pm at + $ a constant. Then

$$-V\frac{\partial V}{\partial x} = \pm\frac{V}{a}\frac{\partial V}{\partial t}; \qquad -V\frac{\partial H}{\partial x} = \pm\frac{V}{a}\frac{\partial H}{\partial t}.$$

Since in a conduit the ratio V/a is usually of the order of $1/100$ or less, the term $V\dfrac{\partial V}{\partial x}$ is negligible when compared with $\partial V/\partial t$ and the term $V\dfrac{\partial H}{\partial x}$ is negligible when compared with $\partial H/\partial t$, as initially assumed. Hence the fundamental equations of waterhammer are acceptable as a valid approximation of the phenomena which exist at any point in the pipe.

III

Velocity of Waterhammer Waves

11. Steel, cast-iron and Transite pipes

The velocity of propagation of pressure waves in a pipe line filled with liquid is defined by Equation (10) of the previous chapter. That is,

$$a = \sqrt{\frac{1}{\frac{w}{g}\left(\frac{1}{K} + \frac{Dc_1}{Ee}\right)}},$$

where values of c_1 are as follows:

$c_1 = \dfrac{5}{4} - \mu$ for a pipe anchored at the upper end and without expansion joints,

$c_1 = 1 - \mu^2$ for a pipe anchored against longitudinal movement throughout its length,

$c_1 = 1 - \dfrac{\mu}{2}$ for a pipe with expansion joints.

Wave velocities for a wide range of D/e ratios for steel, cast-iron, and Transite (cement-asbestos) pipe filled with water are given in Figures 11 and 12.

Since any of the three conditions of longitudinal restraint may be present in the design of steel pipe lines, Figure 11 contains a curve for each of the c_1 values listed above. Cast-iron and Transite (cement-asbestos) [1] pipes are usually buried beneath a fill and the ends of the pipe are often anchored against longitudinal movement. Hence the value for c_1 used in computing the wave velocities in Figure 12 is taken as $1 - \mu^2$. As an example of the use of these diagrams, consider a steel pipe of 40-inch inside diameter and $\frac{1}{4}$-inch wall thickness. If the pipe is fixed at both ends, the wave velocity from Figure 11 is 3020 feet per second.

[1] See Reference 28.

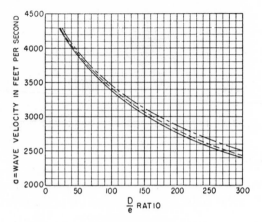

$$a = \sqrt{\dfrac{1}{\dfrac{w}{g}\left(\dfrac{1}{K} + \dfrac{Dc_i}{Ee}\right)}}$$

where:

a = wave velocity (ft. per sec.),

g = acceleration of gravity (ft. per sec²),

$\dfrac{D}{e} = \dfrac{\text{diameter of pipe}}{\text{thickness of pipe}}$,

E = Young's modulus for steel pipes = 4.32×10^9 (lb. per ft²),

K = volume modulus of water = 43.2×10^6 (lb. per ft²),

w = 62.4 = specific weight of water (lb. per ft³),

μ = 0.3.

$c_i = \dfrac{5}{4} - \mu$

$c_i = 1 - \mu^2$

$c_i = 1 - \dfrac{\mu}{2}$

PRESSURE WAVE VELOCITY
IN STEEL PIPES

Figure 11

12. Wood-stave pipes

The pressure wave velocity in wood-stave pipes depends not
only upon the wood making up the staves and the steel of the
bands, but also upon the bending deflection of the wood staves
between the bands, the degree the bands are embedded in the
staves due to the prestress of the bands, and the swelling of
the staves. A high computed value for the wave velocity for wood-
stave pipes is obtainable by neglecting the bending deflection of

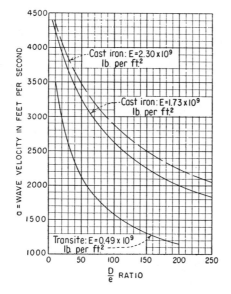

$$a = \sqrt{\dfrac{1}{\dfrac{w}{g}\left(\dfrac{1}{K} + \dfrac{Dc_1}{Ee}\right)}}$$

where:

a = wave velocity (ft. per sec.),

g = acceleration of gravity (ft. per sec².),

$\dfrac{D}{e} = \dfrac{\text{diameter of pipe}}{\text{thickness of pipe}}$,

E = Young's modulus for pipe material (lb. per ft².),

K = volume modulus of water = 43.2×10^6 (lb. per ft².),

$w = 62.4$ = specific weight of water (lb. per ft³.),

$c_1 = 1 - \mu^2$,

$\mu = 0.3$

PRESSURE WAVE VELOCITY IN
CAST IRON AND TRANSITE PIPES

Figure 12

the staves between the bands and assuming that the wood staves and the steel bands act together monolithically. Similarly, a low computed value for the wave velocity is obtainable by assuming that the only members resisting the internal pressure are the steel bands. For the usual materials used in the construction of wood-stave pipes the average ratio of the modulus of elasticity of the wood to that of the steel is about 1 to 30. However, in view of the factors noted above a more accurate wave velocity for wood-stave pipes is obtained by replacing the actual pipe with an equivalent steel pipe whose thickness is determined by adding about one-sixtieth of the wood-stave thickness to an equivalent uniform pipe thickness determined by the steel bands. For example, if 1-inch round bar hoops are spaced at 5-inch intervals on a 60-inch diameter wood-stave pipe whose stave thickness is 3 inches, the equivalent thickness of uniform steel pipe is

$$\frac{3}{60} + \frac{0.785}{5} = 0.21 \text{ inch}$$

and the wave velocity from Figure 11 is 2500 feet per second.

13.   Reinforced concrete pipes

To evaluate the wave velocity for reinforced concrete pipes, an equivalent steel pipe is determined, based on the thickness of concrete and the amount of reinforcing steel in the pipe. The concrete pipe wall thickness is converted into an equivalent steel thickness by multiplying by the ratio of the modulus of elasticity of concrete to the modulus of elasticity of steel. In most instances this ratio varies between the limits $\frac{1}{10}$ and $\frac{1}{15}$. However, since some cracking invariably occurs in concrete pipes, it can be assumed that the ratio is decreased to about $\frac{1}{20}$. Hence, for a concrete pipe of 50 inches inside diameter, and 6-inch wall thickness with $\frac{3}{4}$-inch round reinforcing bars spaced 5 inches from center to center, the equivalent thickness of steel pipe is

$$\frac{6}{20} + \frac{0.44}{5} = 0.39 \text{ inch}.$$

For a pipe fixed against longitudinal movement the wave velocity is 3200 feet per second from Figure 11.

14.   Circular tunnels

The velocity of pressure waves in a circular tunnel used as a pressure conduit is determined in a manner similar to that shown above. The increase in radial deflection of the inner surface of the tunnel under the influence of an increase in pressure $w\,dH$ is[2]

$$\Delta R = \frac{wR}{2G}\,dH,$$

where G is the modulus of rigidity of the material surrounding the tunnel. Then, using a procedure similar to that given in Chapter II, the wave velocity in a circular tunnel is found to be

$$a = \sqrt{\frac{1}{\dfrac{w}{g}\left(\dfrac{1}{K} + \dfrac{1}{G}\right)}}. \tag{17}$$

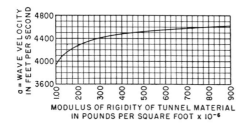

$$a = \sqrt{\frac{1}{\frac{w}{g}\left(\frac{1}{K} + \frac{1}{G}\right)}}$$

where:
  a = wave velocity (ft. per sec.),
  g = acceleration of gravity (ft. per sec.[2]),
  w = 62.4 = specific weight of water (lb. per ft.[3]),
  K = volume modulus of water = 43.2×10^6 (lb. per ft.[2]),
  G = modulus of rigidity of tunnel material (lb. per ft.[2]).

**PRESSURE WAVE VELOCITY
IN CIRCULAR TUNNELS**

Figure 13

Wave velocities in pressure tunnels for various moduli of rigidity are given in Figure 13. For example, for a pressure conduit through a concrete dam where $G = 200 \times 10^6$ pounds per square foot, the wave velocity is found to be 4280 feet per second.

15. Steel-lined circular tunnels

If a steel liner is used in contact with the rock or concrete tunnel, the wave velocity is slightly higher than for an unlined

[2] See Reference 45.

tunnel. The formula for the wave velocity in a steel-lined tunnel is

$$a = \sqrt{\dfrac{1}{\dfrac{w}{g}\left(\dfrac{1}{K} + \dfrac{Dc_2}{Ee}\right)}}, \qquad (18)$$

where

$$c_2 = \frac{Ee}{GD + Ee}.$$

IV

Waterhammer Wave Reflection

16. At a reservoir

Any movement of the control gate at the lower end of the pipe shown in Figure 14 which produces an instantaneous velocity change, will cause a direct pressure wave of the F type to originate in the pipe near the gate. This direct wave moves up the pipe in the direction of positive x with a velocity of a feet per second.

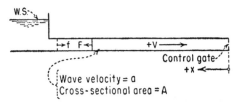

Figure 14

Upon reaching the reservoir a reflected wave of the f type is produced. Initially, the relations between $F(t - x/a)$ and $f(t + x/a)$ are unknown. However, the pressure head at the reservoir end of the pipe is not altered by the transient pressures in the pipe.[1] Then, from Equation (15) at $x = L$,

$$H - H_0 = 0 = F\left(t - \frac{L}{a}\right) + f\left(t + \frac{L}{a}\right),$$

or
$$F\left(t - \frac{L}{a}\right) = -f\left(t + \frac{L}{a}\right). \tag{19}$$

Substituting this relation in Equation (16)

$$V - V_0 = -\frac{2g}{a} F\left(t - \frac{L}{a}\right). \tag{20}$$

---

[1] The wave reflection formulas derived in this section also apply at the free water surface in a surge tank.

25

This equation implies that when an F type direct pressure wave reaches the reservoir, the change in velocity of water at that location is twice that produced by the direct wave at other points in the pipe line. This additional velocity change produces the reflected or f type pressure wave. On the other hand, Equation (19) implies that when an F type pressure wave reaches the reservoir, an f wave is produced at that point. This reflected wave has the same magnitude as the direct wave but is of opposite sign. Hence, at the gate a general relation between F and f is

$$f(t) = -F\left(t - \frac{2L}{a}\right), \tag{21}$$

that is, the reflected wave which reaches the gate is equal in magnitude but of opposite sign to the direct wave which left the gate $2L/a$ seconds earlier.

17. At a dead end

At the dead end of the pipe section shown in Figure 15, $V = V_0 = 0$ at any time t. Then from Equation (16),

$$F\left(t - \frac{L}{a}\right) = f\left(t + \frac{L}{a}\right). \tag{22}$$

Substituting this relation in Equation (15),

$$H - H_0 = 2F\left(t - \frac{L}{a}\right). \tag{23}$$

Thus, at a dead end the pressure wave is entirely reflected without change of sign, and the pressure rise is equal to twice the intensity of the direct pressure wave.

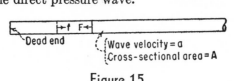

Figure 15

18. At a change in cross-sectional area[2]

Consider the pipe line shown in Figure 16. Equations (15) and (16) as applied to pipe sections BC' and $C''D$ for an F_1 wave reaching the junction C are as follows:

[2] See Reference 10.

$$H_{c't} - H_{c'0} = F_1 + f_1;$$

$$V_{c't} - V_{c'0} = -\frac{g}{a_1}(F_1 - f_1);$$

$$H_{c''t} - H_{c''0} = F_2;$$

$$V_{c''t} - V_{c''0} = -\frac{gF_2}{a_2}.$$

The condition of continuity at junction C is

$$A_2 V_{c''t} = A_1 V_{c't}.$$

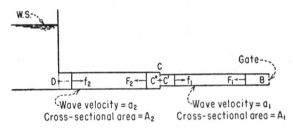

Figure 16

After neglecting the velocity head in the two pipe sections, the solution of the above equations for F_2 and f_1 is

$$F_2 = sF_1; \tag{24A}$$

$$f_1 = rF_1, \tag{24B}$$

where $s - r = 1,$

with $$s = \frac{2A_1/a_1}{A_1/a_1 + A_2/a_2}, \tag{25A}$$

and $$r = \frac{A_1/a_1 - A_2/a_2}{A_1/a_1 + A_2/a_2}. \tag{25B}$$

In these equations s and r are the transmission and reflection factors, respectively. These factors depend upon the cross-sectional area and wave velocity of the two sections of pipe. Since the wave velocity depends on the pipe thickness and properties of the pipe material, a wave reflection occurs at every change in pipe thickness, area, or change in the material of the pipe.

19. At a junction of three or more pipes

In a manner similar to that described above, the transmission and reflection factors at the junction of three or more pipes are also derived. For example, for the branch connection shown in Figure 17,

$$F_2 = F_3 = sF_1; \tag{26A}$$

$$f_1 = rF_1, \tag{26B}$$

where $s - r = 1,$

with $$s = \frac{2A_1/a_1}{A_1/a_1 + A_2/a_2 + A_3/a_3}, \tag{27A}$$

and $$r = \frac{A_1/a_1 - A_2/a_2 - A_3/a_3}{A_1/a_1 + A_2/a_2 + A_3/a_3}. \tag{27B}$$

These equations show that the pressure surges transmitted to the two branches $C''D$ and $C'''E$ are equal irrespective of their cross-sectional areas.

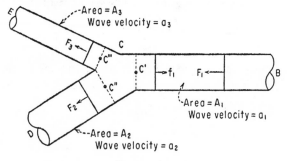

Figure 17

20. At a partially open gate

In Figure 18, let f_1 represent a pressure wave which is moving toward the partially open gate and F_1 represent the pressure wave which is produced at the gate by the reflection of the f_1 wave. From Equations (15) and (16),

$$H - H_0 = F_1 + f_1;$$

$$V - V_0 = -\frac{g}{a}(F_1 - f_1).$$

The discharge of water through the gate is

$$Q = AV = (C_d A_g)\sqrt{2gH},$$

where $(C_d A_g)$ is the effective area of the gate.

Then $\qquad\qquad V = B\sqrt{H},$

where $\qquad\qquad B = \dfrac{(C_d A_g)}{A}\sqrt{2g}.$ \qquad\qquad (28)

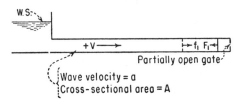

Figure 18

In the above equations V, H, and F_1 are unknown. The solution for V is

$$V = -\frac{aB^2}{2g} + \frac{B}{2}\sqrt{\left(\frac{aB}{g}\right)^2 + 4\left(H_0 + \frac{aV_0}{g} + 2f_1\right)}. \qquad (29)$$

This equation defines the velocity of water in the pipe adjacent to the gate at any time and is expressed in terms of the gate opening and the magnitude of the f_1 wave at the gate. The magnitude of the reflected F_1 wave is determined from Equation (16), that is,

$$F_1 = -\frac{a}{g}(V - V_0) + f_1, \qquad\qquad (30)$$

where $V - V_0$ is the change in the velocity of water in the pipe adjacent to the gate. When Equations (29) and (30) are applied to an f wave at an open gate, the numerical value of F_1 is always less than f_1. Hence pressure waves are partially reflected upon reaching an open gate.

V

Waterhammer for Rapid Gate Movements

21. Instantaneous gate movements[1]

Consider a pipe line in which the flow is initially steady. Assume now that an instantaneous gate closure takes place at the lower end of the pipe. This type of closure will produce a sudden pressure rise in the pipe adjacent to the gate. The magnitude of this pressure rise is determined as follows: Since there is no reflected wave at the gate at the instant of gate closure

$$f\left(t + \frac{x}{a}\right) = 0.$$

Therefore, from Equations (15) and (16),

$$H - H_0 = F\left(t - \frac{x}{a}\right);$$

$$V - V_0 = -\frac{g}{a}F\left(t - \frac{x}{a}\right).$$

Solving these equations for $H - H_0$,

$$H - H_0 = -\frac{a}{g}(V - V_0)$$

or

$$\Delta H = -\frac{a}{g}\Delta V, \tag{31}$$

where ΔV is the change in velocity of water at the gate at the instant the gate movement is completed. This equation is interpreted as follows: A sudden reduction in the water velocity causes an F type pressure wave to form adjacent to the gate. The magnitude of this wave is proportional to the change in the water

[1] See Reference 24.

30

velocity and to the speed of propagation of the pressure wave.

The wave transmission phenomena due to a gate closure is examined more thoroughly in Figure 19.[2] As indicated in this figure an F wave resulting from the sudden complete gate closure moves up the pipe with a velocity of a feet per second. As it passes from lamina to lamina, three concurrent events take place: the velocity of the water behind the wave is reduced to zero, the pipe is expanded, and the density of the water is increased (diagrams b through e). Because of the stretching of the pipe and the increase in the density of the water, the pipe now contains an additional volume of water in excess of that which existed for the steady-state condition. Furthermore, at the time of arrival of the F wave at the reservoir, the pressure inside the pipe near the reservoir end is greater than the static pressure. Because of this unstable condition, water is forced back into the reservoir from the pipe. As a result of this velocity change, a reflected wave is produced at the reservoir end of the pipe which is propagated from the reservoir to the gate (diagrams f through h). Behind the reflected wave, the water flows toward the reservoir, the pipe contracts from its expanded position, and the density of the water is decreased. When the f wave reaches the closed gate, a complete wave reflection occurs, and a second F wave is established of opposite sign to the original direct wave (diagrams i through m). As this wave travels toward the reservoir, further contraction of the pipe and reduction in the density of the water takes place behind the pressure wave. The velocity of the water inside the pipe between the reservoir and the wave front now has the same magnitude and direction as that which existed behind the f wave during its travel to the gate. When the second F wave reaches the reservoir, a second f wave is propagated from this point to the gate (diagrams n through q). The effect of this wave is to again expand the pipe and increase the density of the water. The first wave cycle is complete when the second f wave reaches the gate. A complete wave reflection now occurs at the closed gate and the entire cycle is repeated.

[2] See Reference 13.

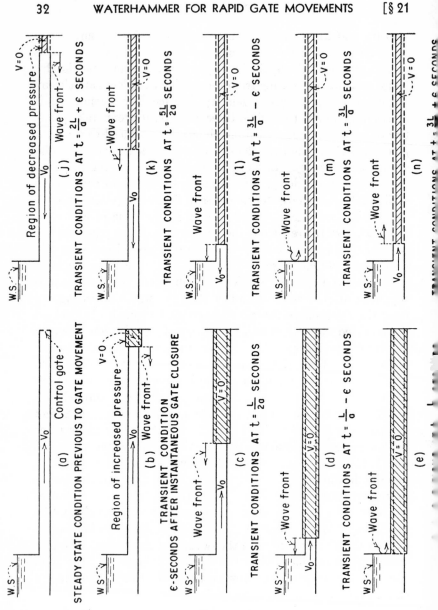

Figure 19

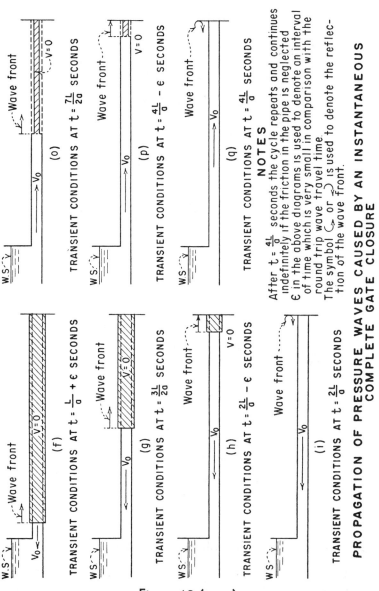

PROPAGATION OF PRESSURE WAVES CAUSED BY AN INSTANTANEOUS COMPLETE GATE CLOSURE

Figure 19 (cont.)

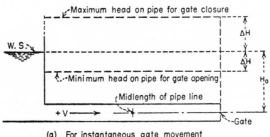

(a) For instantaneous gate movement

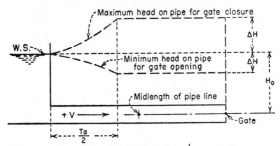

(b) When gate movement time is less than $\frac{L}{a}$ seconds

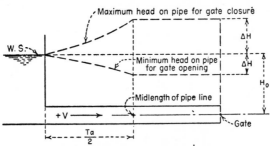

(c) When gate movement time equals $\frac{L}{a}$ seconds

**HEAD CHANGES FOR RAPID
GATE MOVEMENTS**

Figure 20

22. Gate movements completed in less than 2L/a seconds

If the reservoir is at such a distance that a reflected wave cannot return to the gate before the gate motion is completed, the same maximum pressure change occurs at the gate as for an instantaneous gate movement. Hence the physical significance of Equation (31) is further enlarged and stated as follows: For

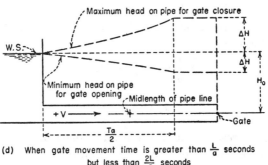

(d) When gate movement time is greater than $\frac{L}{a}$ seconds
but less than $\frac{2L}{a}$ seconds

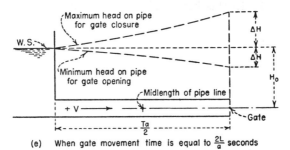

(e) When gate movement time is equal to $\frac{2L}{a}$ seconds

HEAD CHANGES FOR RAPID
GATE MOVEMENTS

Figure 20 (cont.)

an instantaneous gate movement or a gate movement which is
completed in less than $2L/a$ seconds, the maximum change in head
at the gate is the same; that is, $\Delta H = -(a/g)\Delta V$. For any gate
movement which takes place in less than $2L/a$ seconds, the maximum change in head extends from the gate to a certain limiting
point along the pipe. This limiting point is determined as follows:[3] If x_2 is the distance from the limiting point to the reservoir, the wave-travel time from the gate to the limiting point is
$(L - x_2)/a$ seconds. The time required for the pressure wave to
travel from the gate to the reservoir and back to the limiting
point is $(L + x_2)/a$ seconds. If the total gate movement time is
T, the elapsed time from the start of the gate movement to the
instant of arrival of the final incremental pressure change at the

[3] See Reference 30.

limiting point is $T + (L - x_2)/a$. Therefore the limiting point is located along the pipe where the direct wave is met by the reflected wave, that is,

$$\frac{L + x_2}{a} = T + \frac{L - x_2}{a}$$

or
$$x_2 = \frac{Ta}{2}. \tag{32}$$

A pictorial representation of the head changes along the pipe for gate movement time equal to or less than $2L/a$ seconds is shown in Figure 20. In this figure $\Delta H = -\dfrac{a}{g}\Delta V$ as defined by Equation (31).

VI

Waterhammer for Slow Gate Movements

23. Basic considerations

When the gate movement time is equal to or less than $2L/a$ seconds, the maximum pressure change at the gate is determined from Equation (31) since no reflected waves return to the gate soon enough to alter the pressure at that location. However, when the gate movement time is greater than $2L/a$ seconds, this

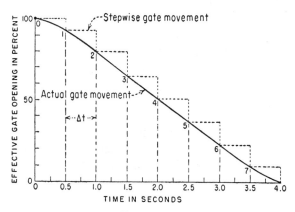

Figure 21

is no longer true. For long gate movements the actual movement is approximated by a series of successive instantaneous stepwise movements.[1] These stepwise movements are selected so that they have the exact value of the actual gate opening at the time of completion of each step as shown in Figure 21. The pressure in-

[1] See Reference 16.

37

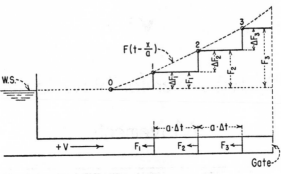

Figure 22

crements produced at the gate by each of these stepwise movements are then displaced from one another by a distance $a\Delta t$ as
shown in Figure 22.

24. Time intervals used in computations

In order to reduce the computations to a minimum, the selected time interval should be as large as possible. After an instantaneous gate movement takes place at the lower end of the
pipe, a reflected wave returns to the gate $2L/a$ seconds later.
Hence the maximum time interval which can be used in the computations to determine the waterhammer at the control gate is
the complete round trip wave travel time of the pipe, that is $2L/a$
seconds. If the pressure-time history at any other point on the
pipe line is desired, the largest time interval which can be used
in the computations is the shortest round trip wave travel time
from the point on the pipe to a point of wave reflection. If more
values are desired on the pressure-time-history curve for any particular point on the pipe, smaller time intervals are necessary.
However, this will not result in a more accurate determination of
the waterhammer for the points on the pressure-time history previously determined with the larger time intervals. This is due to
the fact that since the time interval used in the computations is
not greater than $2L/a$ seconds, Equation (31) applies. Therefore
the head change at the end of a particular time interval depends
only upon the velocity of water at the beginning and end of the
time interval under consideration. In general, the time of occur-

rence of the maximum pressure change at the various points in the pipe line will not coincide with the instants of time selected for the stepwise representation of the actual gate movement. Hence, if the gate movement is very irregular, smaller time intervals must be used in the computations.

25. Example

Consider a pipe line of uniform diameter and thickness as shown in Figure 23. At this installation the gate is closed in 6 seconds in a manner specified in Figure 24.

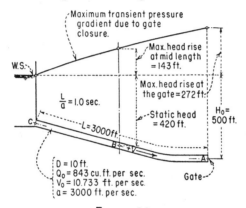

Figure 23

The following relations which were derived above are used in the waterhammer computations:

At any point on the pipe away from the gate

$$H - H_0 = F + f. \tag{15}$$

At the gate

$$B = \frac{(C_d A_g)}{A} \sqrt{2g}; \tag{28}$$

$$V = -\frac{aB^2}{2g} + \frac{B}{2} \sqrt{\left(\frac{aB}{g}\right)^2 + 4\left(H_0 + \frac{aV_0}{g} + 2f\right)}; \tag{29}$$

$$F = -\frac{a}{g}(V - V_0) + f; \tag{30}$$

$$f(t) = -F\left(t - \frac{2L}{a}\right). \tag{21}$$

A summary of the waterhammer computations is shown in Table 1. The values given in the various columns in this table are obtained in the following manner: The time $t = 0$ is taken at the start of the gate movement, and time intervals of 1 second as shown in column 1 are selected for the computations in order to determine the head rise at the mid-length of the pipe. Values

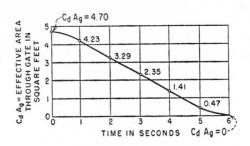

GATE CLOSURE TIME RELATION

Figure 24

of $C_d A_g$ are read directly from Figure 24 and are recorded in column 2. Values of B are then computed for each 1-second time interval and recorded in column 3. This completes the first three columns of the table. In the remaining computations it is necessary to compute successively the values of V, F, f and $(F + f)$ for each of the times listed in the first column. For example, for

TABLE 1

1	2	3	4	5	6	7
TIME t, SECONDS	$C_d A_g$	B	V	F	f	HEAD RISE, (F + f)
0	4.70	0.480	10.733	0	0	0
1	4.23	0.432	10.162	53.2	0	+53
2	3.29	0.336	8.777	182.2	0	+182
3	2.35	0.240	6.669	325.3	-53.2	+272
4	1.41	0.144	3.982	446.7	-182.2	+265
5	0.47	0.048	1.296	553.9	-325.3	+229
6	0	0	0	553.3	-446.7	+107
7	0	0	0	446.1	-553.9	-108
8	0	0	0	446.7	-553.3	-107
9	0	0	0	553.9	-446.1	+108
10	0	0	0	553.3	-446.7	+107
11	0	0	0	446.1	-553.9	-108
12	0	0	0	446.7	-553.3	-107
13	0	0	0	553.9	-446.1	+108
14	0	0	0	553.3	-446.7	+107

$t = 1$ second the value of V is determined from Equation (29) using the value of $B = 0.432$ and $f = 0$. The computed value of $V = 10.162$ feet per second is recorded in column 4. The magnitude of the direct wave F at $t = 1$ second is then computed from Equation (30). This computed value of 53.2 feet is recorded in column 5. The magnitude of the f waves which reach the gate are then obtained from Equation (21). These values are recorded in column 6. At the time $t = 1$ second no reflected wave has returned to the gate so that $f = 0$. From Equation (15) the head rise at the gate is the sum of the F and f waves which are present at the gate. This value is recorded in column 7. For $t = 1$

TABLE 2

1	2	3	4
t	F	f	HEAD RISE AT MIDLENGTH (F + f)
0	0	0	0
0.5	0	0	0
1.5	53.2	0	+53
2.5	182.2	−53.2	+129
3.5	325.3	−182.2	+143
4.5	446.7	−325.3	+121
5.5	553.9	−446.7	+107
6.5	553.3	−553.9	−1
7.5	446.1	−553.3	−107
8.5	446.7	−446.1	+1
9.5	553.9	−446.7	+107
10.5	553.3	−553.9	−1
11.5	446.1	−553.3	−107
12.5	446.7	−446.1	+1
13.5	553.9	−446.7	+107
14.5	553.3	−553.9	−1

second, the head rise is 53 feet. Similar computations are made for the terms V, F, and f for $t = 2, 3, 4$, etc., thus completing the tabulation.

In Table 2 an account has been kept of the waves which reach the mid-length of the pipe line at various times. Since the first instantaneous movement of the gate is completed at $t = 1$ second and the wave travel time from the gate to the mid-length of the pipe is 0.5 second, the first direct F wave of magnitude 53.2 feet reaches the mid-length of the pipe at $t = 1.5$ seconds. This value is recorded in column 2. This F wave reaches the reservoir at $t = 2$ seconds and the reflected wave arrives at the mid-length at $t = 2.5$ seconds as an f wave of opposite sign as recorded in column 3. In a similar manner the sum of all the F and f waves which reach the mid-length of the pipe are recorded in the tabulation.

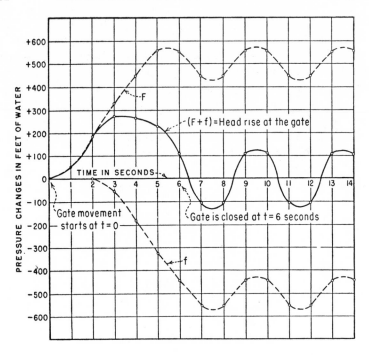

TIME HISTORY OF THE PRESSURE CHANGES
IN THE PIPE LINE ADJACENT TO THE GATE

Figure 25

26.   Interpretation of solution

The phenomenon of waterhammer in a uniform pipe line for gate closure is seen to consist of successive pressure waves of both the F and f type which surge up and down the pipe as changes in velocity occur at the gate. For the example shown, these waves are initially positive but upon traveling up the pipe to the reservoir they are reflected as negative pressure waves which return toward the gate, where they are again reflected. The summation of these waves of alternating magnitude at the gate at any particular time gives the rise or fall in pressure produced by the gate movement.

In the above problem time intervals of 1 second were selected between successive stepwise gate movements to approximate the

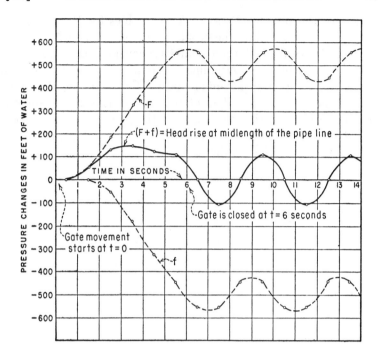

**TIME HISTORY OF THE PRESSURE CHANGES
AT THE MIDLENGTH OF THE PIPE LINE**

Figure 26

actual gate movement. The gate opening at the end of each of these time intervals corresponds to the actual gate opening. Hence the tabulation given in Table 1 gives correct values at each instant of time shown. To find the correct values for other instants of time would require a recomputation, using smaller time intervals. However, to aid in visualizing the changes in the magnitude of the pressure waves and the pressure rise caused by this wave action, the values of each 1-second time interval are connected by smooth curves as shown in Figures 25 and 26. In the present problem such curves represent very good approximations for the head rise at any time, since the gate motion specified in Figure 24 is a smoothly varying function.

The maximum head rise in the pipe adjacent to the gate is computed as 272 feet, and the maximum head rise at the mid-

length of the pipe is 143 feet.   These values for the maximum
head rise are plotted on the profile of the pipe line and a smooth
curve is drawn through these points as shown in Figure 23.   Such
a curve is useful in determining the required pipe thickness to
withstand safely the maximum head.   For example, the maximum head in the pipe adjacent to the gate is 772 feet and the
maximum head at the mid-length of the pipe is 563 feet.   It is
noted that the maximum head rises at these two points in the
pipe line do not occur at the same time.

VII

Theory of Graphical Waterhammer Analysis for Gate Operation

27. Conjugate waterhammer equations[1]

The analytical waterhammer solution shown in the preceding chapter gives an indication of the extent of the computations involved in obtaining a solution by that method. In general, the necessity of calculating the term V accurately from Equation (29) makes the method a tedious one. A considerable increase in computations also results when there are physical discontinuities in the pipe line. In order to obtain the waterhammer solution more readily, a graphical method of analysis is used. The method is derived as follows: The fundamental waterhammer equations are

$$H - H_0 = F\left(t - \frac{x}{a}\right) + f\left(t + \frac{x}{a}\right); \tag{15}$$

$$V - V_0 = -\frac{g}{a}\left[F\left(t - \frac{x}{a}\right) - f\left(t + \frac{x}{a}\right)\right]. \tag{16}$$

Subtracting Equation (16) from (15) gives

$$H - H_0 = \frac{a}{g}(V - V_0) + 2F\left(t - \frac{x}{a}\right). \tag{33}$$

The addition of Equations (15) and (16) gives

$$H - H_0 = -\frac{a}{g}(V - V_0) + 2f\left(t + \frac{x}{a}\right). \tag{34}$$

Since Equation (33) contains only the F wave term, this equation defines the velocity and head relations in the pipe line in terms of F waves. Similarly, Equation (34) defines the velocity and head relations in terms of f waves.

[1] See Reference 3.

45

Consider the pipe line shown in Figure 27. The lower section of pipe is of uniform diameter and thickness and has a wave velocity of a_1 while the upper section of pipe has a wave velocity of a_2 feet per second. Suppose that there is an F_1 wave at B_1 at time t_1. This wave moves up the pipe with a velocity of a_1 feet

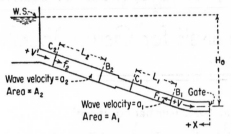

Figure 27

per second and reaches C_1 at $t_2 = t_1 + L_1/a_1$ seconds. Similarly, suppose that there is an f_2 wave at C_2 at time t_3. This wave moves down the pipe with a velocity of a_2 feet per second and reaches B_2 at $t_4 = t_3 + L_2/a_2$ seconds. Equation (33) is now applied at B_1 and C_1 while Equation (34) is applied at B_2 and C_2 as follows:

$$H_{B_1t_1} - H_{B_1t_0} = \frac{a_1}{g}(V_{B_1t_1} - V_{B_1t_0}) + 2F_1;$$

$$H_{C_1t_2} - H_{C_1t_0} = \frac{a_1}{g}(V_{C_1t_2} - V_{C_1t_0}) + 2F_1;$$

$$H_{C_2t_3} - H_{C_2t_0} = -\frac{a_2}{g}(V'_{C_2t_3} - V'_{C_2t_0}) + 2f_2;$$

$$H_{B_2t_4} - H_{B_2t_0} = -\frac{a_2}{g}(V'_{B_2t_4} - V'_{B_2t_0}) + 2f_2.$$

After eliminating F_1 and f_2 from these equations and using the relations

$$H_{B_1t_0} = H_{C_1t_0}, \qquad H_{C_2t_0} = H_{B_2t_0},$$
$$V_{B_1t_0} = V_{C_1t_0}, \qquad V'_{B_2t_0} = V'_{C_2t_0},$$

the following equations are obtained:

$$H_{B_1t_1} - H_{C_1t_2} = \frac{a_1}{g}(V_{B_1t_1} - V_{C_1t_2}); \tag{35}$$

$$H_{C_2t_3} - H_{B_2t_4} = -\frac{a_2}{g}(V'_{C_2t_3} - V'_{B_2t_4}). \tag{36}$$

In the derivation of Equations (35) and (36), B_1 and C_1 are arbitrary points on the lower section of uniform pipe, while B_2 and C_2 are arbitrary points on the upper section of uniform pipe. Hence these equations are applicable between any two points, including the end points, of any section of uniform pipe in the pipe line.

These equations are rewritten in another form involving the following ratios:

$$h = \frac{H}{H_0};$$

$$v = \frac{V}{V_0} = \frac{V'}{V'_0} \quad \text{for gate closing movements;}$$

$$v = \frac{V}{V_e} = \frac{V'}{V'_e} \quad \text{for gate opening movements,}$$

where V_0 and V'_0 are the initial steady velocities of water in the pipe sections prior to gate closure, and V_e and V'_e are the final steady velocities of water after gate opening has been completed. Then

$$h_{B_1 t_1} - h_{C_1 t_2} = 2\rho_1(v_{B_1 t_1} - v_{C_1 t_2}); \tag{37}$$

$$h_{C_2 t_3} - h_{B_2 t_4} = -2\rho_2(v_{C_2 t_3} - v_{B_2 t_4}), \tag{38}$$

where for gate closure,

$$\rho_1 = \frac{a_1 V_0}{2g H_0} \quad \text{and} \quad \rho_2 = \frac{a_2 V'_0}{2g H_0},$$

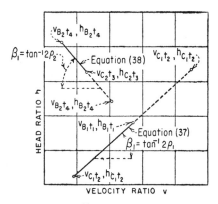

Figure 28

and for gate opening,

$$\rho_1 = \frac{a_1 V_e}{2gH_0} \quad \text{and} \quad \rho_2 = \frac{a_2 V_e'}{2gH_0}.$$

Equations (37) and (38) are the conjugate waterhammer equations, while ρ_1 and ρ_2 are the pipe line constants. On a rectangular coordinate system of h and v the conjugate equations are represented by straight lines which have a slope of $\pm 2\rho$ and pass through known points as shown in Figure 28.

28. Gate discharge equations

Each conjugate waterhammer equation defines the relation between h and v at a point in a uniform pipe line in terms of h and v at another point in the pipe under the action of the waterhammer wave phenomena. In order to determine h and v explicitly, a second independent relation is required. For gate operations this relation is determined from the discharge at the gate. The initial discharge through the gate under steady conditions is

$$V_{A_0} = B_0 \sqrt{H_{A_0}};$$

and the discharge at any gate opening and head as defined by Equation (28) is

$$V_A = B \sqrt{H_A}.$$

Then
$$v_A = \tau \sqrt{h_A}, \tag{39}$$

where $v_A = \dfrac{V_A}{V_{A_0}}, \quad h_A = \dfrac{H_A}{H_{A_0}}, \quad \text{and} \quad \tau = \dfrac{B}{B_0}.$

Although Equation (39) has been derived for gate closure, an identical equation results for gate opening by letting $\tau = B/B_e$, where B_e is the gate opening factor at the end of the gate movement.

29. Graphical solution for gate closure

Consider the pipe line and the gate closure relation shown in Figures 29a and b. This problem is identical to that solved by analytical methods in the previous chapter. In order to illustrate the solution in its simplest form, the head rise at the gate is determined for 2-second time intervals. Since the wave travel time from A to E is 1 second, the necessary conjugate waterhammer equations for the end points of the pipe line are as follows:

$$
\begin{aligned}
h_{A_0} - h_{E_1} &= +2(v_{A_0} - v_{E_1}); &\text{(a)}\\
h_{E_1} - h_{A_2} &= -2(v_{E_1} - v_{A_2}); &\text{(b)}\\
h_{A_2} - h_{E_3} &= +2(v_{A_2} - v_{E_3}); &\text{(c)}\\
h_{E_3} - h_{A_4} &= -2(v_{E_3} - v_{A_4}); &\text{(d)}\\
h_{A_4} - h_{E_5} &= +2(v_{A_4} - v_{E_5}); &\text{(e)}\\
h_{E_5} - h_{A_6} &= -2(v_{E_5} - v_{A_6}), &\text{(f)}
\end{aligned}
\tag{40}
$$

etc.

In these equations the head and velocity ratios h and v at the gate are indicated at $t = 0$, 2, 4, and 6 seconds. Hence only the discharge relation at the gate at these specific times will be required in the waterhammer solution. These are as follows:

$$
\begin{aligned}
v_{A_0} &= 1.0 \sqrt{h_{A_0}}; &\text{(m)}\\
v_{A_2} &= 0.7 \sqrt{h_{A_2}}; &\text{(n)}\\
v_{A_4} &= 0.3 \sqrt{h_{A_4}}; &\text{(o)}\\
v_{A_6} &= 0; &\text{(p)}\\
v_{A_t} &= 0 \text{ when } t > 6 \text{ seconds.}
\end{aligned}
\tag{41}
$$

Equations (40) and (41) are now solved simultaneously by graphical methods as follows: On a set of coordinate axes of v and h, parabolas m, n, o, and p are drawn for values of $\tau = 1.0$, 0.7, 0.3, and 0, as shown in Figure 29c. The parabola $\tau = 0$ coincides with the vertical axis at $v = 0$. The point A_0 prior to the gate movement is located at the coordinates $h = 1$, $v = 1$. Since the effect of a gate movement does not reach the reservoir end of the pipe until after the wave travel time of 1 second, E_1 is also located at the same point as A_0. Equation (40a) is then represented as a point on the diagram at $h = 1$, $v = 1$. Equation (40b) is the equation of a straight line with a slope of -2ρ which passes through the point E_1. Since the point corresponding to A_2 is concurrently located on the parabola n and the sloping line b, it must be located at the intersection of these two lines as shown in the figure. Equation (40c) is the equation of a straight line of slope 2ρ which passes through the point A_2. For a constant reservoir level E_3 is located on the horizontal axis at $h = 1$. The

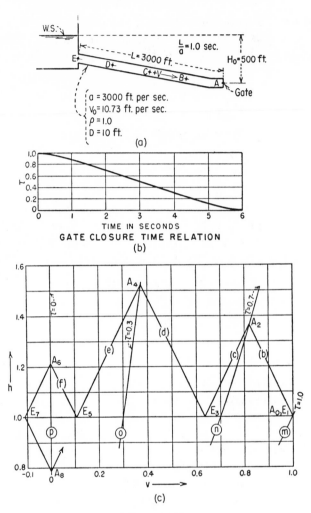

Figure 29

points corresponding to A_4, E_5, A_6, E_7, A_8, etc., are then determined in the manner shown in the figure.

A comparison of the results of this solution with those of the analytical method given in the preceding chapter shows that the results obtained from the two methods are identical. The graphical method of waterhammer analysis is seen to consist essentially of the graphical solution of simultaneous equations. One group of equations depends upon the values of τ, the effective gate opening, which is specified. These gate relations are represented by parabolas on the h-v diagram. A second group of equations is obtained from the conjugate waterhammer equations. These equations are represented on the h-v diagram by straight lines of slope $\pm 2\rho$. The intersections of the sloping lines and parabolas determine the head and velocity ratios at the gate and the intersections of the sloping lines with the horizontal line $h = 1$ determines these ratios at the reservoir end of the pipe.

VIII

Waterhammer Produced by Gate

Closure

30. At the mid-length of pipe

The graphical method of waterhammer analysis is extended to determine the head changes at the mid-length of the pipe for the example used in the preceding section. Time intervals of 1 second are used in the computations, and parabolas corresponding to values of τ for these time intervals are shown on the h-v diagram in Figure 30. Conjugate waterhammer equations at 1-

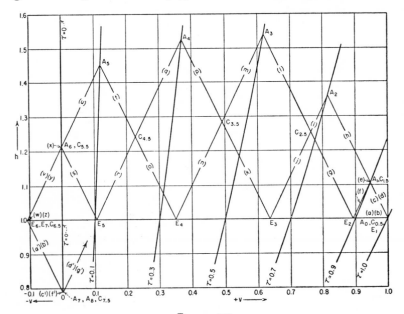

Figure 30

second time intervals are now required for the pipe sections AC and CE. Instead of writing these equations formally as in the preceding chapter, a tabular representation of the equations can be used as shown in Table 3. In this table $t = 0, 1, 2, 3, 4$, etc., are shown in the column directly below the gate at A. The times recorded in the center column at C, the mid-length of the pipe, are equal to times recorded at the gate plus one-half second, the

TABLE 3

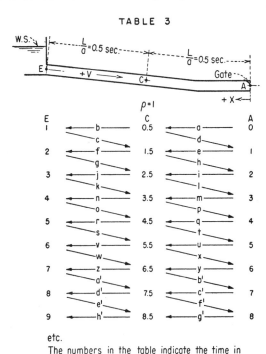

etc.

The numbers in the table indicate the time in
    seconds after the start of gate closure
    of the points A, C or E.

wave travel time between the gate and the mid-length of the pipe. Similarly, the times recorded under E, at the reservoir end of the pipe, are the times recorded at the mid-length plus one-half second. The lines with arrows represent conjugate waterhammer equations and the direction of travel of the pressure waves.

From a consideration of the action of the initial direct and reflected waves, A_0, $C_{0.5}$, and $E_{1.0}$ are located at a common point at $h = 1$, $v = 1$. Then $A_{1.0}$ and $C_{1.5}$ are located at the intersection of the line of slope -2ρ and the parabola corresponding to $\tau = 0.9$. The graphical representation of the remaining conjugate equations is shown in Figure 30 with the segments of the sloping lines marked according to the designation shown in Table 3. The maximum head rise at the gate as obtained from these computations is $0.54H_0$ and occurs at $t = 3$ seconds, while the maximum head rise at the mid-length is $0.28H_0$ and occurs at $t = 3.5$ seconds.

31. At the quarter points of the pipe line

The graphical method of analysis is now extended to determine the pressure changes at other points in the pipe line. In general it is necessary to select points on the pipe line which divide it into an integral number of pipe sections of equal wave travel time. The maximum time interval used in the computations is then the round trip wave travel time for any pipe section. For example, in order to determine the pressure changes at the quarter points in the pipe line shown in Figure 29a, one-half second time

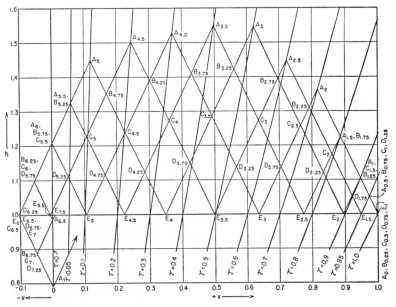

Figure 31

intervals are used. The solution then determines simultaneously the pressure changes at the gate, the one-quarter point, the midpoint, and the three-quarter point of the pipe line for one-half second time intervals as shown in Figure 31.

32. Pipe line with a stepwise change in diameter

In using the conjugate equations in the waterhammer solution the factors which are considered are ρ, the pipe line constant, and the wave travel time between two points in a uniform section of the pipe line. For a pipe line which has a stepwise change in the cross-sectional area or wave velocity, these conjugate equa-

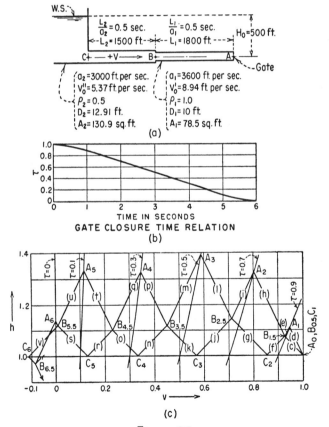

Figure 32

tions are also applicable at the end points of each section of uniform pipe. On the h-v diagram the graphical representation of these equations is similar to that shown in the preceding section with the exception that one set of the conjugate equations is represented by lines of slope $\pm 2\rho_1$, while the other set has a slope of $\pm 2\rho_2$. For example, consider the pipe line shown in Figure 32a and the gate closure time relation shown in Figure 32b. The round trip wave travel time in pipe sections AB and BC is 1 sec-

TABLE 4

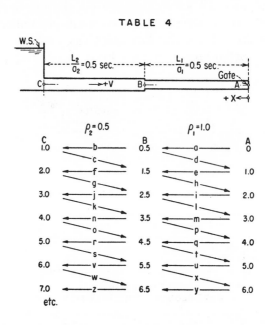

ond. Therefore the largest time interval which can be used in the computations is 1 second. Parabolas corresponding to the values of τ for 1-second time intervals are shown on the h-v diagram in Figure 32c. The applicable conjugate equations for 1-second time intervals for the pipe sections AB and BC are indicated in Table 4. This tabulation differs from Table 3 only in the respect that the value of ρ is different in the two sections of pipe. The graphical representation of these conjugate equations is shown in Figure 32c.

There is no particular difficulty in obtaining a waterhammer solution when the round trip wave travel times in each of the two sections are different as shown for the pipe line in Figure 33. The method is also applicable when there are more than two stepwise changes in the diameter or wave velocity in the pipe line. How-

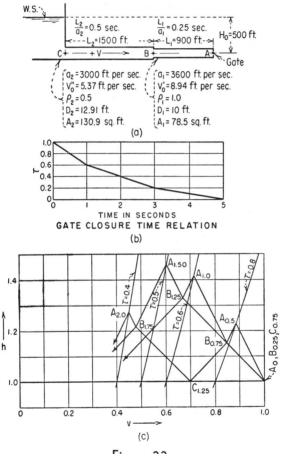

Figure 33

ever, when there are many stepwise changes in the pipe line this method becomes too tedious. In such cases the approximate method given in Chapter XV is useful and of sufficient accuracy for most purposes.

33. Partial gate closure

When the control gate is closed only part way and held there, the waterhammer solution is as shown in Figure 34. This solution shows that although pipe line friction has been neglected, the partial reflections which occur at the open gate cause the pressure and velocity in the pipe to return quickly to a steady value.

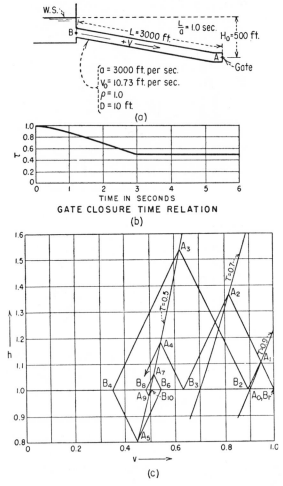

Figure 34

34. Gate closure with a relief valve[1]

Consider a pipe line which has a relief valve near the control gate as shown in Figure 35a. The type of relief valve which is considered is often used in turbine penstock installations for the control of waterhammer, and is operated in such a manner that the relief valve opens as the turbine gates are closing. A short time later the relief valve closes at a much slower rate with a negligible rise in pressure. The assumed combined effective gate

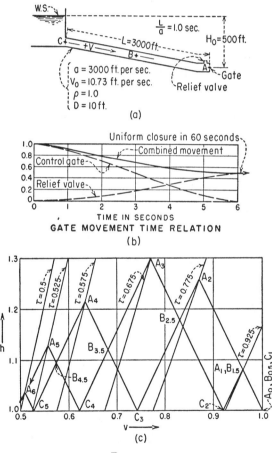

(a)

(b)

(c)

Figure 35

<hr />

[1] See Reference 40.

opening of the control gate and relief valve is shown in Figure 35b. Since the waterhammer effects depend only upon the changes in velocity of water in the penstock, the waterhammer solution is obtained from the combined effective gate opening as shown in Figure 35c.

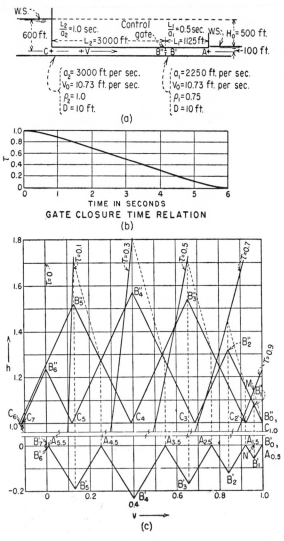

Figure 36

35. Control gate located away from outlet end of pipe

Consider the pipe line shown in Figure 36a and the gate closure shown in Figure 36b. Since the largest common round trip wave travel time which occurs in both sections of the pipe is 1 second, this time interval is used in the waterhammer computations. The discharge through the gate varies with $\sqrt{h_{B''t} - h_{B't}}$. As the gate is closed, pressure waves form at B' and B'', which move toward A and C. In the waterhammer solution B_0'' and C_1 are located at $h = 1$, $v = 1$, while B_0' and $A_{0.5}$ are located at $h = 0$, $v = 1$ as shown in Figure 36c. A line is now drawn from $C_{0.5}$ (this is the same point as C_1) which has a slope of $-2\rho_2 = -2$ on which B_1'' is to be located. Similarly, a line is drawn from $A_{0.5}$ which has a slope of $+2\rho_1 = 1.5$ on which B_1' is to be located. Since the flow on both sides of the control valve are equal, B_1'' and B_1' are located on the same vertical line. Moreover, these two points are located in such a manner that the vertical distance from the point B_1'' to the parabola corresponding to $\tau = 0.9$ is the same as the vertical distance from the horizontal line $h = 0$ to $B_{1.0}'$, that is, $B_1'N = B_1''M$. The reason for this is that at $t = 1.0$ second, the flow through the gate is

$$v_{B'_1} = v_{B''_1} = 0.9\sqrt{h_{B''_1} - h_{B'_1}}.$$

A simple method for locating the points $B_{1.0}'$ and $B_{1.0}''$ is illustrated by the dotted lines in Figure 36c. Starting from B_0'' draw a dotted line of slope $-2(\rho_1 + \rho_2)$ which intersects the parabola corresponding to $\tau = 0.9$ at the point M. Then $B_{1.0}'$ and $B_{1.0}''$ are located on the vertical line which passes through the point M. Other points which are required in the solution are determined in a similar manner as shown in the figure.

36. Control gate located at upper end of pipe

Consider the pipe line installation shown in Figure 37a and the gate closure time relation in Figure 37b. For this installation $h_{B''t} = 1.0$. Hence, the waterhammer solution shown in Figure 37c is obtained by locating the points B_2', B_4', B_6', etc., so that on the same vertical line the distance $B''M$ above the horizontal line

$h = 1$ to the parabola for each gate opening is equal to $B''B'$ below the line $h = 1$. The solution indicates that the maximum drop in head at the gate is $0.53H_0$ and the maximum head rise is $0.22H_0$.

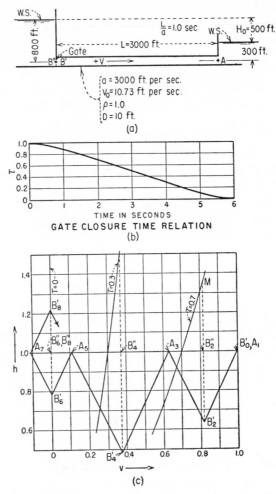

Figure 37

IX

Waterhammer Produced by Gate Opening

37. Fall in pressure produced by gate opening[1]

When the flow of water in a pressure conduit is retarded, the kinetic energy of the water is converted into potential energy as evidenced by an increase in the hydrostatic pressure. Conversely, when the flow of water in a closed conduit is increased, energy is supplied to set the water in motion, with a consequent reduction in the hydrostatic pressure. For example, consider the pipe line shown in Figure 38a and the effective gate opening shown in Figure 38b. Parabolas corresponding to the values of τ for 1-second time intervals are shown in Figure 38c. The initial velocity of water in the pipe is zero and hence the starting point of the graphical solution on the h-v diagram is at the point $h = 1$, $v = 0$. This locates the point for A_0, $B_{0.5}$, and $C_{1.0}$. The graphical waterhammer solution is then completed as shown in the figure.

38. Pressure rise produced by gate opening

After the initial drop in pressure due to a gate opening, a pressure rise above normal occurs because of the reflected waterhammer waves which return from the reservoir. For example, consider the pipe line shown in Figure 39a and the gate opening shown in Figure 39b. The waterhammer solution for the pressure changes at the gate is shown in Figure 39c from which it is seen that at $t = 6$ seconds the pressure rise is $0.10H_0$.

The maximum head rise due to a gate opening occurs when an initially closed gate is opened to its final position in $2L/a$ sec-

[1] See References 1 and 25.

onds or less and held there. To illustrate this, consider the pipe line shown in Figure 40a and the gate movement shown in Figure 40b, for which the graphical waterhammer solution is shown in Figure 40c. The maximum head rise at the gate due to the return of the reflected waves from the reservoir is $0.23H_0$ and occurs at

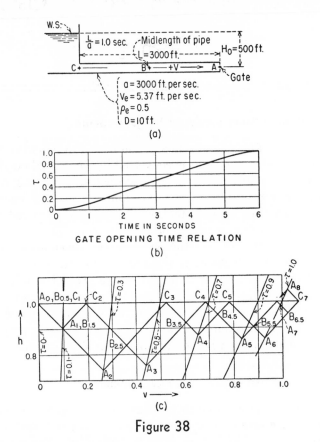

Figure 38

$t = 4$ seconds. For this type of gate opening the head rise depends only upon the pipe line constant ρ_e. Hence the results of waterhammer solutions of this type can be indicated on a chart as shown in Figure 41. From this figure it is seen that the maximum head rise produced by a gate opening from zero gate is $0.23H_0$.

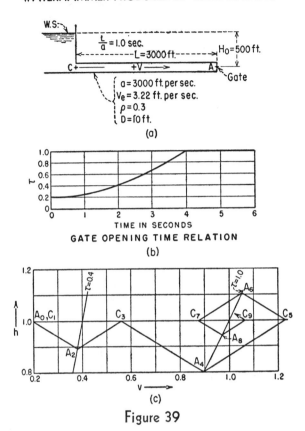

Figure 39

39. Rhythmic opening and closure of control gate[2]

Under certain conditions of gate operation, it is possible to obtain a rhythmic opening and closure of the regulating gate. Such conditions have been observed, for example, in hydraulic turbine installations due to governor action. If the gate motion is in phase with the motion of the waterhammer waves in the pipe line an appreciable head rise can occur. For example, consider the pipe line shown in Figure 42a and the gate movement time history shown in Figure 42b, for which the waterhammer solution is shown in Figure 42c. This solution indicates a maximum head rise of $1.24H_0$ at the gate when a complete cycle of gate operation

[2] See References 1 and 21.

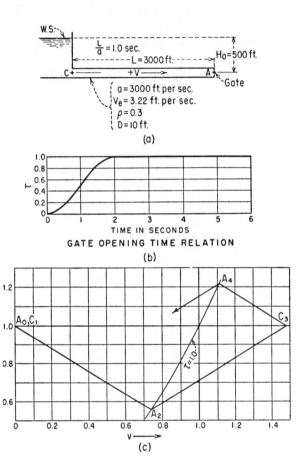

(a)

(b)

GATE OPENING TIME RELATION

(c)

Figure 40

is performed in $4L/a$ seconds. Since the head rise due to this type of gate movement depends only upon the parameter ρ_e, the results of all possible solutions are indicated on a chart as shown in Figure 43. From this figure it is seen that as ρ_e increases, the maximum head rise approaches $2H_0$ as a limit.

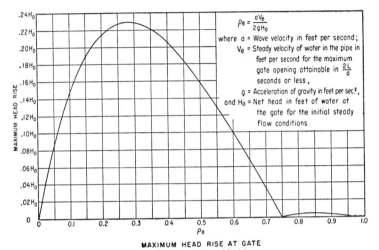

MAXIMUM HEAD RISE AT GATE
DUE TO GATE OPENING

Figure 41

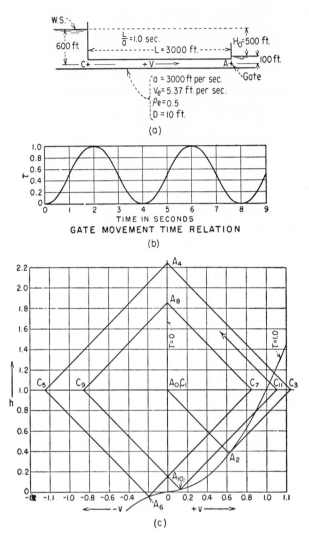

Figure 42

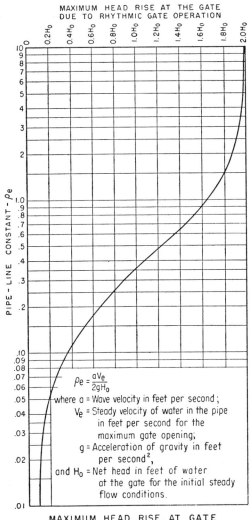

MAXIMUM HEAD RISE AT THE GATE
DUE TO RHYTHMIC GATE OPERATION

PIPE - LINE CONSTANT - ρ_e

$\rho_e = \dfrac{aV_e}{2gH_0}$

where a = Wave velocity in feet per second;

V_e = Steady velocity of water in the pipe
in feet per second for the
maximum gate opening;

g = Acceleration of gravity in feet
per second²,

and H_0 = Net head in feet of water
at the gate for the initial steady
flow conditions.

MAXIMUM HEAD RISE AT GATE
DUE TO RHYTHMIC GATE OPERATION

Figure 43

X

Waterhammer for Uniform Gate Operation

40. Uniform gate closure to zero gate

The graphical method of waterhammer analysis given in the preceding chapters provides a method for determining the head changes at various points in a pipe line for any type of gate movement. When the effective gate opening varies uniformly with respect to time, the gate motion is called uniform gate operation. For this type of gate motion it is not necessary to make a graphical waterhammer analysis for each pipe line and gate closure, because the results of a large number of waterhammer solutions can be shown on charts. Figure 44 shows one of these charts for uniform gate closure to zero gate.[1] In order to determine the maximum head rise at the gate, it is necessary to calculate the pipe line characteristic ρ and the time of gate closure in terms of the number of $2L/a$ intervals, that is

$$N = \frac{Ta}{2L}. \tag{42}$$

The value of K is then read from the chart and the head rise determined from the relation

$$\Delta H = 2\rho K H_0. \tag{43}$$

When $N \leq 1$, that is, when the complete gate closure is performed during a time equal to or less than $2L/a$ seconds, $K = 1$ and $\Delta H = 2\rho H_0$. For such rapid gate closures the head rise is also equal to $-\dfrac{a}{g} \Delta V$ as defined by Equation (31).

[1] See References 1 and 36.

70

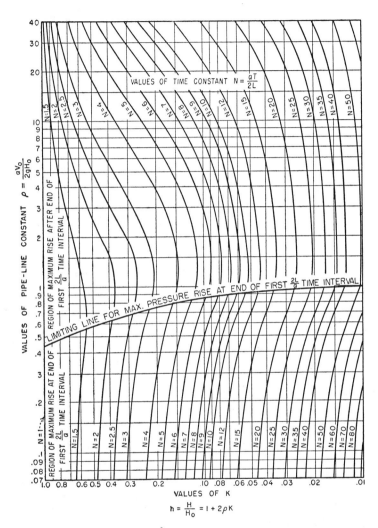

RAY S. QUICK'S WATERHAMMER CHART
FOR UNIFORM GATE OPERATION

Figure 44

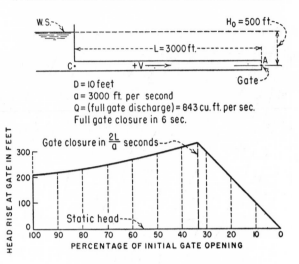

HEAD RISE AT GATE DUE TO UNIFORM CLOSURE
FROM VARIOUS INITIAL GATE OPENINGS

Figure 45

If the gate closure can be accomplished from any initial gate position at the same uniform rate, the maximum head rise at the gate occurs when the uniform gate closure takes place in exactly $2L/a$ seconds. This is illustrated for a typical case in Figure 45.

41.   Uniform gate opening from zero gate[2]

When the effective gate opening from the zero gate position is uniform with respect to time, the minimum head at the gate is found to occur at exactly $2L/a$ seconds after the start of the gate movement. If the gate opening starts from the zero gate position,

$$h_{min} = (-K + \sqrt{K^2 + 1})^2, \tag{44}$$

where $K = LV_e/gH_0T$. In this equation V_e is the final steady velocity of water in the pipe after the gate opening has been completed. The equation is applicable when $T \gtreqless 2L/a$ seconds and its solution is facilitated by the use of Figure 46. When $T \leq 2L/a$ seconds, the head change is equal to $-\dfrac{a}{g}\Delta V$ as defined by Equation (31).

[2] See Reference 25.

$$h_{min.} = \frac{H_{min.}}{H_0}$$

where $H_{min.}$ = minimum head at the gate in feet,
$\qquad H_0$ = initial steady head at the gate in feet,
$\qquad L$ = length of pipe in feet,
$\qquad T$ = time for opening gate to the desired position
$\qquad\qquad$ in seconds $\left(T \geqq \frac{2L}{a}\right)$,
$\qquad V_e$ = final steady velocity in the pipe in feet per
$\qquad\qquad$ second after gate opening,
and g = acceleration of gravity in feet per second^2.

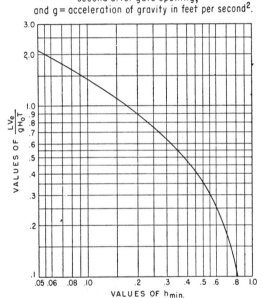

MINIMUM HEAD AT GATE DUE TO
UNIFORM GATE OPENING FROM
THE CLOSED POSITION

Figure 46

XI

Waterhammer in Pump Discharge Lines Caused by Power Failure

42. Transient conditions at pump and discharge line[1]

There are many operating conditions at large motor-driven centrifugal pump installations which are capable of producing substantial pressure changes in the discharge lines. Of these conditions one of the most important is the rapid deceleration of the pump motors because of a power failure. Figure 47 shows the time history of the pressure, flow, and speed changes at a pump installation produced by power failure at the pump motors. When the power supply to the pump motor is suddenly cut off, the only energy that is left to drive the pump in the forward direction is the kinetic energy of the rotating elements of the motor and pump and the entrained water in the pump. Since this energy is usually small when compared with that required to maintain the flow against the discharge head, the reduction in pump speed is quite rapid. As the pump speed reduces, the flow of water in the discharge line adjacent to the pump is also reduced. As a result of these rapid flow changes, waterhammer waves of subnormal pressure are formed in the discharge line at the pump. These subnormal pressure waves move rapidly up the discharge line to the discharge outlet, where a wave reflection occurs. Soon the speed of the pump is reduced to a point where no water can be delivered against the existing head. If there is no control valve present at the pump, the flow through the pump reverses, although the pump may be still rotating in the forward direction. The speed of the pump now drops more rapidly and passes through zero speed. A short time later the pump, acting as a

[1] See References 3, 33, 34, and 35.

turbine, reaches runaway speed in reverse. As the pump approaches runaway speed, the reverse flow through the pump reduces rapidly, and this reduction in the flow produces a pressure rise at the pump and along the length of the discharge line.

In order to determine the transient hydraulic conditions at the pump and discharge line subsequent to a power failure at the

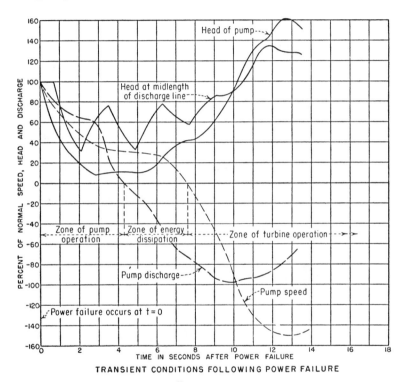

TRANSIENT CONDITIONS FOLLOWING POWER FAILURE

Figure 47

pump motor, three effects must be considered; namely, the pump and motor inertia, the pump characteristics, and the waterhammer wave phenomena in the discharge line. The effect of the pump and motor inertia is obtained from the inertia equation. This equation defines the relation between the pump speed and torque at a given instant of time in terms of the kinetic energy of the rotating system. The pump characteristics are obtained from a complete pump characteristic diagram. This diagram de-

fines the manner in which the pump torque and speed vary with
the head and discharge throughout the range of operation as a
pump, energy dissipator, and turbine. Finally, the waterhammer
effects are obtained from the waterhammer equations. These
equations define the relations between the head and flow in the
discharge line during the transient flow conditions under the action of the waterhammer waves.

43. Inertia equation

When the power to the pump motor is suddenly cut off, the
deceleration of the pump at any instant depends upon the fly-
wheel effect of the rotating parts of the pump and motor and the
instantaneous torque exerted by the pump impeller. For a rotating system the accelerating torque is equal to the product of
the mass moment of inertia of the rotating system and the angular
acceleration. Following a power failure at the pump motor, the
decelerating torque on the rotating system corresponds to the
pump torque. If the decelerating torque is taken as positive,

$$M = -I \frac{d\omega}{dt} = -\frac{WR^2}{g} \frac{d\omega}{dt}. \tag{45}$$

For a small time interval $\Delta t = t_2 - t_1$, this equation is written
approximately as follows:

$$\frac{M_1 + M_2}{2} = -\frac{WR^2}{g} \cdot \frac{(\omega_2 - \omega_1)}{\Delta t}$$

$$= \frac{2\pi WR^2}{60g} \cdot \frac{N_1 - N_2}{\Delta t}. \tag{46}$$

This equation is written with the ratios $\alpha = N/N_R$ and
$\beta = M/M_R$ as follows:

$$\alpha_1 - \alpha_2 = \frac{15gM_R}{\pi WR^2 N_R} (\beta_1 + \beta_2)\Delta t. \tag{47}$$

The decelerating torque at the rated head and pump speed is

$$M_R = \frac{60wH_RQ_R}{2\pi N_R\eta_R}. \tag{48}$$

Then $$\alpha_1 - \alpha_2 = K_1(\beta_1 + \beta_2)\Delta t, \tag{49}$$

where $$K_1 = \frac{450gwH_RQ_R}{\pi^2 WR^2\eta_R N_R^2} = \frac{91,600H_RQ_R}{WR^2\eta_R N_R^2}. \tag{50}$$

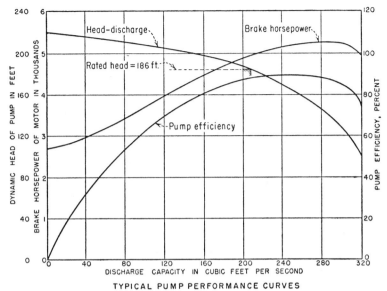

TYPICAL PUMP PERFORMANCE CURVES

Figure 48

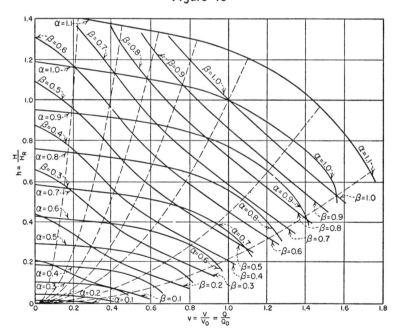

CHARACTERISTIC DIAGRAM FOR REGION OF
NORMAL PUMP OPERATION

Figure 49

44. Pump characteristics[2]

Typical pump performance data usually supplied by the pump manufacturer are shown in Figure 48 and include the head, brake horsepower, and efficiency plotted against the discharge. These data are converted to a family of torque and speed curves on an h-v diagram in the following manner: Referring to Figure

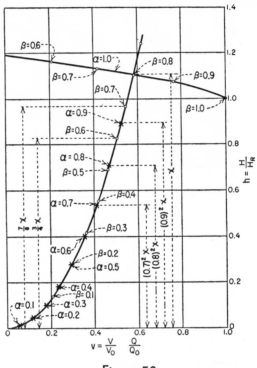

Figure 50

49, the point corresponding to the rated head and discharge of the pump has the coordinates $h = 1$, $v = 1$. The curves for $\alpha = 1$ and $\beta = 1$ also pass through this point on the diagram, since these ratios are defined in terms of rated values. Other values of β on the curve for $\alpha = 1$ are determined by computing values of h and v from the brake horsepower curve given in Figure 48. Points on

[2] See Reference 39.

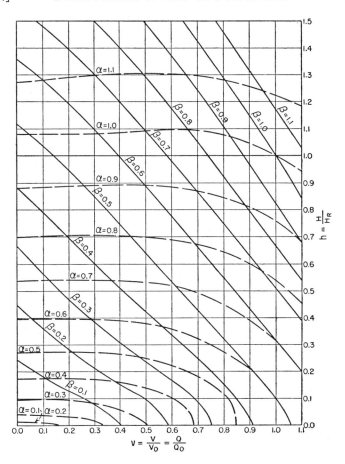

PUMP CHARACTERISTICS DIAGRAM
ZONE OF NORMAL PUMP OPERATION

Figure 51a

the diagram for other values of α and β are then determined from the laws of homologous pump operation. For example, for a given pump, H and M vary with N^2, while N and $\sqrt{H}$ vary with Q. To use these relations on the h-v diagram a parabola of the type $h = K_2 v^2$ is passed through a known point on the diagram such as that shown in Figure 50 at $\alpha = 1.0, \beta = 0.8$. The vertical distance $h = 1.10$ at this point is then divided into eight equal parts, and the points corresponding to $\beta = 0.7, 0.6$, etc. are lo-

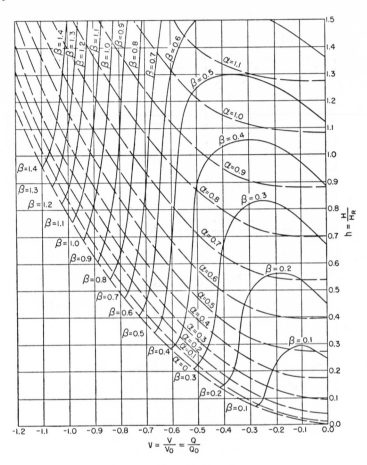

PUMP CHARACTERISTICS DIAGRAM
ZONE OF ENERGY DISSIPATION

Figure 51b

cated on the parabola at ordinate values of $h = \frac{7}{8}(1.10)$, $\frac{6}{8}(1.10)$, etc. Similarly, points corresponding to $\alpha = 0.9$ and 0.8 are located on the same parabola at values of $h = 1.10(0.9)^2$ and $1.10(0.8)^2$. A smooth curve is then drawn through the points on the various parabolas corresponding to each value of α and β. Figure 49 shows families of torque and speed curves which were constructed in this manner.

The pump characteristics shown in Figure 49 are for the zone

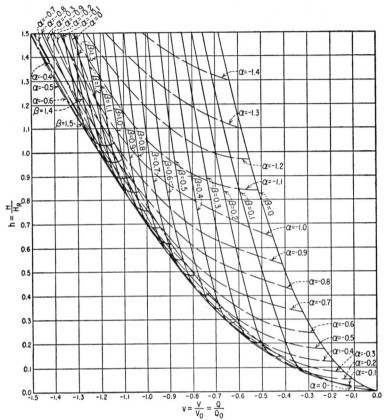

PUMP CHARACTERISTICS DIAGRAM
ZONE OF TURBINE OPERATION

Figure 51c

of normal pump operation. When power failure occurs at the pump motor, these characteristics are adequate for determining the minimum transient pressures at all points in the discharge line and for determining the likelihood of water column separation. However, after the flow reverses through the pump, additional pump characteristics are required for the zone of energy dissipation in which the pump is running in the forward direction with the flow through the pump in reverse, and for the zone of turbine operation, in which the flow through the pump and the pump rotation are both in reverse. Complete characteristics for a single suction pump in each of the three zones of operation as determined from actual test data are shown in Figures 51a, b, and c.[3]

45. Waterhammer equations

The waterhammer equations for the pump discharge line shown in Figure 52 are as follows:

$$h_{B_1 t_1} - h_{C_1 t_2} = -2\rho_1(v_{B_1 t_1} - v_{C_1 t_2}), \qquad (51A)$$

$$h_{C_2 t_3} - h_{B_2 t_4} = +2\rho_2(v_{C_2 t_3} - v_{B_2 t_4}). \qquad (51B)$$

In these equations $(t_2 - t_1)$ is the wave travel time between B_1 and C_1 for an F_1 type pressure wave, and $(t_4 - t_3)$ is the wave travel time between C_2 and B_2 for an f_2 type pressure wave. For a uniform discharge line, $\rho = aV_0/2gH_R$, the pipe line constant.

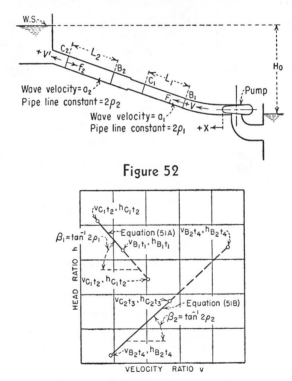

Figure 52

Figure 53

[3] See Reference 29.

These equations define the relations between the head and velocity ratios during the waterhammer wave phenomena. On a coordinate system of h and v, these equations are represented by straight lines which have a slope $\pm 2\rho$ as shown in Figure 53. Each waterhammer equation gives one relation between h and v at a point in a uniform section of the discharge line in terms of h and v which are known at another point in the line. In order to determine h and v explicitly, a second independent relation is required. This relation is obtained from the pump-inertia equation with the use of the pump characteristic diagram.

46. Graphical waterhammer analysis

Consider the pumping plant installation shown in Figure 54. If a power failure occurs at all three pump motors, $2\rho = 2.31$ and $K_1 = 0.224$. For a time interval $\Delta t = L/4a$,

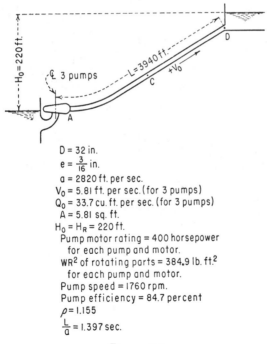

D = 32 in.
$e = \frac{3}{16}$ in.
a = 2820 ft. per sec.
V_0 = 5.81 ft. per sec. (for 3 pumps)
Q_0 = 33.7 cu. ft. per sec. (for 3 pumps)
A = 5.81 sq. ft.
$H_0 = H_R = 220$ ft.
  Pump motor rating = 400 horsepower
    for each pump and motor.
  WR^2 of rotating parts = 384.9 lb. ft.^{2}
    for each pump and motor.
  Pump speed = 1760 rpm.
  Pump efficiency = 84.7 percent
  $\rho = 1.155$
  $\frac{L}{a} = 1.397$ sec.

Figure 54

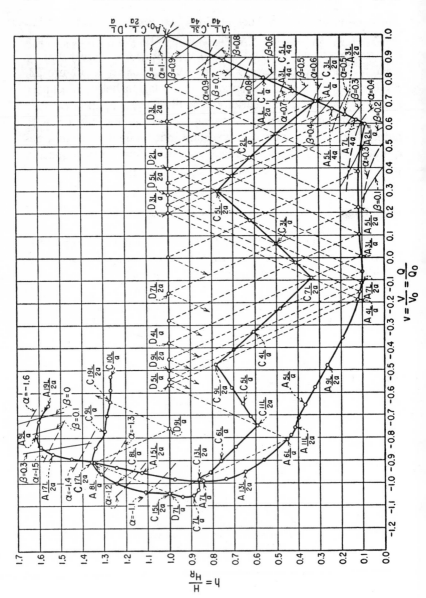

Figure 55

$$\alpha_1 - \alpha_2 = K_1\Delta t(\beta_1 + \beta_2) = 0.0782(\beta_1 + \beta_2). \qquad (52)$$

The simultaneous solution of the waterhammer equations and the inertia equations on the pump characteristics diagram by graphical methods is shown in Figure 55. The complete pump characteristics used in this solution are those shown in Figures 51a, b, and c. The starting point in the solution corresponding to A_0 is located on the h-v diagram at the coordinates $h = 1$, $v = 1$. $A_{L/4a}$ is then located on the line of slope $2\rho = +2.31$ which passes

TABLE 5

PUMP SPEED AND TORQUE RATIOS

LOCATION	β (TORQUE RATIO)	α (SPEED RATIO)	$\alpha_1 - \alpha_2$ (FROM CURVES)	$\alpha_1 - \alpha_2$ (FROM EQUATION 52)
A_0	1.000	1.000	0	0
$A_{\frac{L}{4a}}$	0.760	0.863	0.137	0.138
$A_{\frac{L}{2a}}$	0.610	0.755	0.108	0.107
$A_{\frac{3L}{4a}}$	0.520	0.668	0.087	0.088
$A_{\frac{L}{a}}$	0.440	0.592	0.076	0.075
$A_{\frac{5L}{4a}}$	0.380	0.528	0.064	0.064
$A_{\frac{3L}{2a}}$	0.325	0.472	0.056	0.055
$A_{\frac{7L}{4a}}$	0.285	0.425	0.047	0.047
$A_{\frac{2L}{a}}$	0.250	0.383	0.042	0.042
$A_{\frac{9L}{4a}}$	0.170	0.350	0.033	0.033

through A_0 in the following manner: The location of $A_{L/4a}$ is first estimated. Values of α_2 and β_2 are then read from the pump characteristics curves. This value of β_2 is used in Equation (52) to compute α_2. If the computed value of α_2 does not agree with the value of α_2 on the curves, the point for $A_{L/4a}$ is shifted up or down on the sloping line $2\rho = +2.31$ until these values of α_2 agree. This particular point is found to be located at a value of $\beta = 0.760$ and $\alpha = 0.863$. Other points for $A_{L/2a}$, $A_{3L/4a}$, etc., are determined in a similar manner. The values for several of these points are shown in Table 5 and the graphical waterhammer solution is completed as shown in Figure 55, from which the following limiting values are read:

Maximum drop in head at pump
$$= 0.92H_0 = 202 \text{ feet.}$$

Maximum drop in head at mid-length of discharge line
$$= 0.69H_0 = 152 \text{ feet.}$$

Maximum head rise at pump
$$= 0.61H_0 = 134 \text{ feet.}$$

Maximum head rise at mid-length of discharge line
$$= 0.35H_0 = 77 \text{ feet.}$$

A time history of the head, flow, and speed changes as obtained from the graphical solution is shown in Figure 47.

47. Water column separation

The maximum positive and negative pressure changes obtained from the waterhammer solution are plotted on the discharge line profile in Figure 56 to show the limiting pressures for

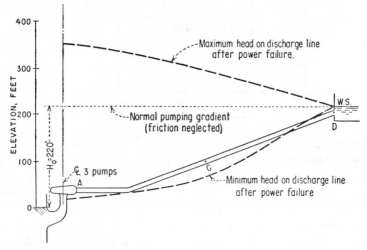

Figure 56

which the discharge line should be designed. When the minimum pressure at any point along the pump discharge line reaches the vapor pressure of water, the waterhammer solution is no longer valid. If this subatmospheric pressure condition inside the pipe persists for a sufficient period, the liquid water column parts and is separated by a section of vapor. Water column separation sometimes occurs during the initial negative surge waves on long pump discharge lines at high points which are near the hydraulic gradient. Wherever possible, this condition should be avoided by using either a surge tank, air chamber, or larger motor WR^2 because of the high pressure created when the two liquid water columns rejoin. When water column separation cannot be avoided, special means must be taken to minimize the violence of impact due to the rejoining of the water columns. This can be accomplished by positioning special control valves or other protective devices which will either reduce the reverse velocity of the upper column or increase the reverse velocity of the lower water column.

48. Waterhammer charts[4]

In obtaining the graphical waterhammer solution for a pump installation subsequent to a power failure at the pump motors, two independent parameters are used with the complete pump characteristics. These are ρ, the pipe line constant, and $K_1(2L/a)$ a constant which includes the effect of the pump and motor inertia and the waterhammer wave travel time of the discharge line. For a given set of pump characteristics, the results of a large number of waterhammer solutions can be shown on charts as indicated in Figures 57a to h. These charts furnish a convenient method for obtaining the limiting transient conditions at the pump and discharge line when no control valves are present at the pump. Although the charts are theoretically applicable to one particular type of pump operating at the rated head prior to power failure, they are very useful for obtaining the approximate waterhammer effects in any pump discharge line.

[4] See References 12, 33, and 34.

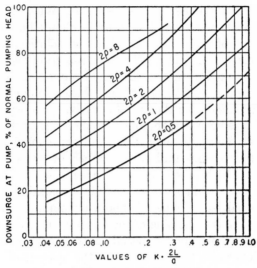

DOWNSURGE AT PUMP

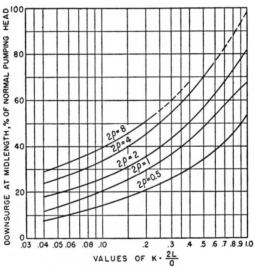

DOWNSURGE AT MIDLENGTH

Figure 57a, b

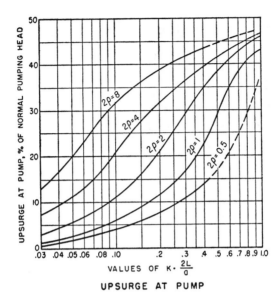

UPSURGE AT PUMP

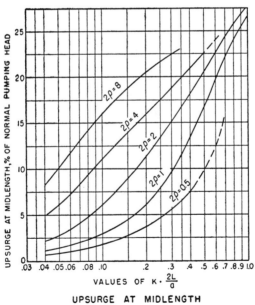

UPSURGE AT MIDLENGTH

Figure 57c, d

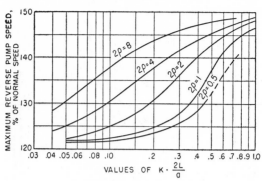

MAXIMUM REVERSE SPEED

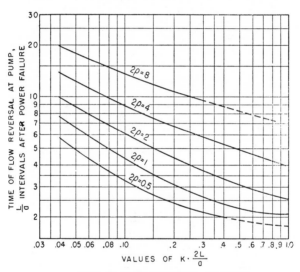

TIME OF FLOW REVERSAL AT PUMP

Figure 57e, f

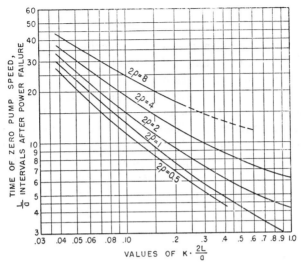

TIME OF ZERO PUMP SPEED

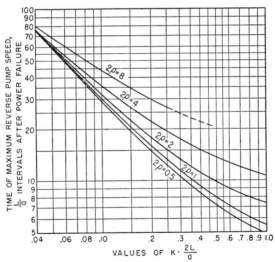

TIME OF MAXIMUM REVERSE PUMP SPEED

Figure 57g, h

49. Conclusions

Pressure surges in pump discharge lines subsequent to a power failure at the pump motors can be computed accurately if the complete characteristics of the pump are known. In most cases only the characteristics for the zone of normal pump operation are obtainable from the pump performance data supplied by the pump manufacturer. This permits an accurate determination of the waterhammer effects up to the point at which the flow reverses through the pump. When necessary, pump characteristics for the zones of energy dissipation and turbine operation can be estimated with sufficient accuracy for waterhammer purposes.

XII

Special Waterhammer Solutions
for Pump Discharge Lines

50. Effect of changes in pumping head

Consider the installation shown in Figure 58. This is the same installation as that shown in Figure 54 with the intake water surface elevation 22 feet higher. The initial pumping head,

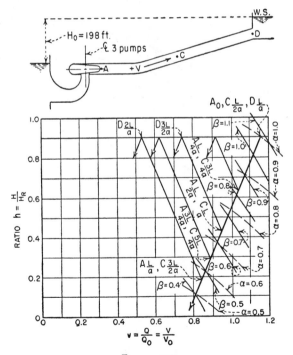

Figure 58

$$H_0 = 198 \text{ feet} \quad \text{and} \quad h_0 = \frac{H_0}{H_R} = 0.90.$$

The waterhammer solution for this installation due to a power failure at the pump motors is shown in Figure 58. This solution is obtained in a manner similar to that shown in Figure 55 with the exception that the starting point A_0, $C_{L/a}$ is located at the intersection of the lines $h = 0.90$ and $\alpha = 1.0$.

51. Pump discharge line with check valve[1]

For a pump discharge line with a swing check valve on the discharge side of the pump, the normal discharge of the pump

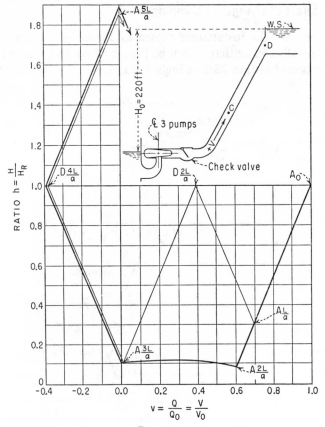

Figure 59

[1] See Reference 38.

keeps the check valve open. However, when the flow through the pump reverses subsequent to a power failure, the swing check valve closes rapidly. The waterhammer analysis for such an installation is shown in Figure 59. This is the same installation as that shown in Figure 54 with the addition of check valves on the discharge side of the pumps. The first part of the solution is the same as that shown in Figure 55 until zero discharge is reached. At this moment the check valve is assumed to close rapidly and

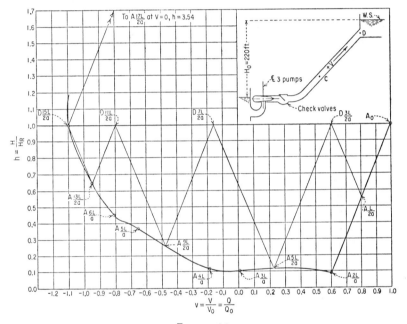

Figure 60

the waterhammer effects are then determined on the same basis as for a dead end. The maximum head rise at the check valve is found to be $0.90H_0$ as compared with $0.61H_0$ when the reverse flow passes through the pump.

In the event that the check valve closure is delayed, the head rise at the check valve may be higher. For example, in Figure 60 it is assumed that the check valve closes rapidly at $13L/2a$ seconds after power failure. The maximum head rise at the pump for this delayed valve closure is $2.54H_0$ as compared with $0.90H_0$ for the earlier closing check valve.

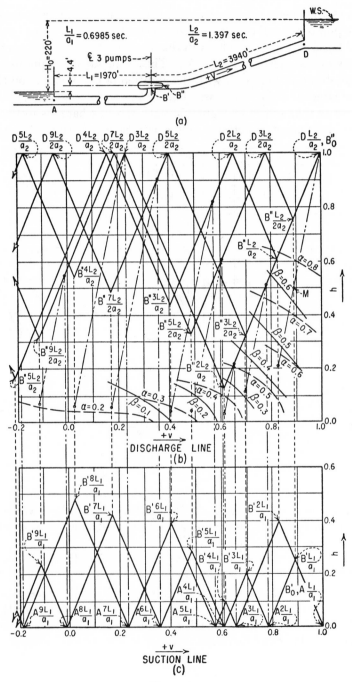

Figure 61

52.   Pump discharge line with long suction line

Consider the installation shown in Figure 61a. This is the same installation as that shown in Figure 54 with the addition of a long suction line. When the pumps operate with a pressure head of H_B'' on the discharge side and a head of H_B' on the suction side, the pump discharge depends upon the pumping head $H = H_B'' - H_B'$. Upon power failure at the pump motors, pressure waves of subnormal pressure form at B'' on the discharge side of the pump, which move toward the discharge outlet at D, and positive pressure waves form at B' on the suction side of the pump and move toward the intake at A. In the graphical water-hammer solution of this problem a time interval of $L_1/a_1 = L_2/2a_2$ seconds is used in the computations. Now B_0'' and D_{L_2/a_2} are located at $h = 1$, $v = 1$, while B_0' and A_{L_1/a_1} are located at $h = 0$, $v = 1$ as shown in Figures 61b and c. A line is now drawn from the point D_{L_2/a_2}, which has a slope of $+2\rho_2 = +2.31$, on which the point corresponding to $B_{L_2/2a_2}''$ is located. Similarly a line is drawn from the point A_{L_1/a_1} which has a slope of $-2\rho_1 = -2.31$ on which the point corresponding to B_{L_1/a_1}' is located. One of the requirements for locating the points $B_{L_2/2a_2}''$ and B_{L_1/a_1}' is that since $v_{B''L_2/2a_2} = v_{B'L_1/a_1}$, these points are located on the same vertical line. Another requirement is that at $t = L_1/a_1$ seconds, the change in pump speed must satisfy Equation (49) for a pumping head of $(h_{B''L_2/2a_2} - h_{B'L_1/a_1})$. A simple graphical method for locating the points $B_{L_2/2a_2}''$ and B_{L_1/a_1}' is illustrated by the dotted lines in Figures 61b and c. Starting from the point D_{L_2/a_2} draw a dotted line whose tangent is $+2(\rho_1 + \rho_2)$. On this dotted line determine by trial the point on the pump curves which satisfies Equation (49). For example, the point corresponding to $t = L_1/a_1$ is located at the point M, where $\alpha = 0.745$. The points corresponding to $B_{L_2/2a_2}''$ and B_{L_1/a_1}' are then located on the vertical line which passes through the point M. The remaining points for other time intervals are determined in a similar manner.

53.   Effect of control valves

There are many types of pressure control valves in current use at pumping plant installations. The methods of waterhammer analysis which are given in the preceding chapters are readily applied to include the effect of any type of control valve which may be used. However, the time and manner in which the control valve acts must be known as well as the flow characteristics of the valve for the various degrees of opening. For the condition of power failure at the pump motors the graphical waterhammer solution is performed initially on the pump characteristics diagram, using the inertia and waterhammer equations with the

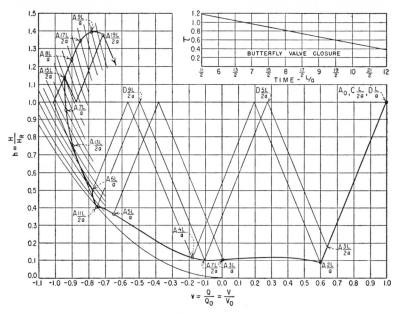

Figure 62

pump characteristics in the manner described above until the flow is controlled by the control valve. The graphical solution is then completed with the waterhammer equations and parabolas corresponding to the flow through the control valve.

Figures 59 and 60 show the effects of rapidly closing check valves. When the valve closure is slower, the latter part of the graphical solution is performed with parabolas in the manner shown in Figure 62. This figure shows the effect of slow closing valves which control the flow at $11L/2a$ seconds after power failure. This is the same installation as that shown in Figure 54, with the addition of the controlled valve closure after power failure.

54. Starting and stopping pumps

The waterhammer effects due to the normal starting of pumps are usually relatively small. However, these effects can be further minimized by the use of proper control valves or start-

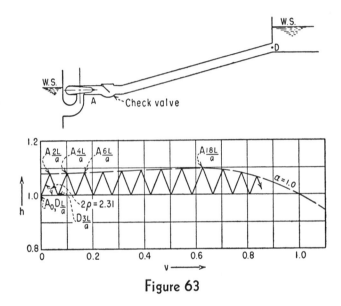

Figure 63

ing equipment, and by insuring that all air is removed from the discharge lines. If there is a shutoff valve on the discharge side of the pump, the pump is brought up to speed with the discharge valve closed. The discharge valve is then slowly opened with no appreciable waterhammer effect in the discharge line. In taking the pump out of service the waterhammer effect is also negligible if the discharge valve is closed slowly before shutting off the power to the pump motor.

If there are only swing check valves on the discharge side of the pumps, a nominal head rise occurs if the pumps are started rapidly. This effect is shown in Figure 63 for starting three pumps simultaneously. This is the same installation as that shown in Figure 54 with the addition of check valves. In this solution it is assumed that the starting up time of the pumps is less than the round trip wave travel time of the discharge line. The starting point A_0, $D_{L/a}$ in the graphical solution is located at $h = 1$, $v = 0$. Point $A_{2L/a}$ is then obtained by drawing a line of slope $+2\rho$ from $D_{L/a}$ until it intersects the curve $\alpha = 1.0$. Other points in the graphical solution are obtained in the manner shown in Figure 63.

XIII

Waterhammer Analysis
Including Effect of Hydraulic Losses

55. Losses concentrated at intake[1]

In the derivation of the fundamental waterhammer equations for the elastic water column theory in Chapter II, it was assumed that the velocity head and hydraulic losses were negligible when compared with the head changes. This assumption is justified for the majority of the pipe lines where rapid changes in flow are most likely to occur. Occasionally, however, it is necessary to include the effect of these hydraulic losses in the waterhammer computations. If the velocity head and the hydraulic losses are assumed to vary with V^2, the effect of these losses can be included in the waterhammer equations by the introduction of a V^2 term in Equation (7), the equation of equilibrium for an element of water. However, the simultaneous solution of the resulting equation with Equation (8), the equation of continuity for an element of water, is not possible.[2]

For pipe lines involving gate movements, a first approximation to the effect of the hydraulic losses is obtained in the waterhammer solution by a hypothetical obstruction located at the upper end of the pipe line. This obstruction has the same total head loss as the entire pipe line. For example, consider the pipe line shown in Figure 64a and the gate closure time relation shown in Figure 64b. The entrance loss, pipe line friction, and velocity head in the pipe line for the initial flow is $H_f = 13.4$ feet, from which

$$h_f = \frac{H_f}{H_0}\left(\frac{V}{V_0}\right)^2 = 0.028v^2,$$

[1] See Reference 4.
[2] See Reference 47.

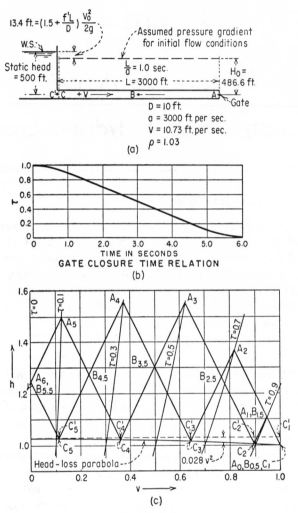

Figure 64

as shown by the head loss parabola in Figure 64c. In the graphical waterhammer solution shown in this figure the hypothetical obstruction is located at C. Hence, points for C'_t are located on the horizontal dotted line at $h = 1.028$ and points for C_t are located on the head-loss parabola. The graphical waterhammer solution using the head-loss parabola is completed as shown in the figure.

56. Losses concentrated at pump discharge outlet

For a pump discharge line the effect of the hydraulic losses in the entire line can be approximated in the waterhammer solution by a hypothetical obstruction at the discharge outlet. For example, consider the installation shown in Figure 65. This is the

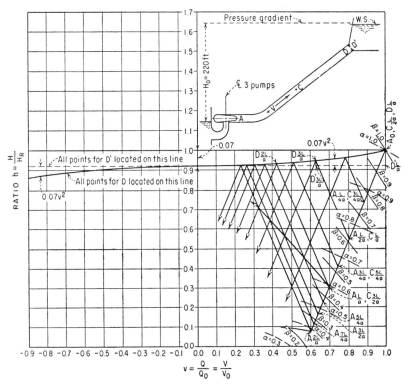

Figure 65

same installation as that shown in Figure 54. For this installation $h_f = 0.07v^2$ and $h_D = 1 - 0.07(1 - v^2)$ for normal pump flow and $h_D = 1 - 0.07(1 + v^2)$ when the flow reverses through the pump. These head-loss relations are shown in Figure 65 together with the graphical waterhammer analysis following a power failure at the pump motors.

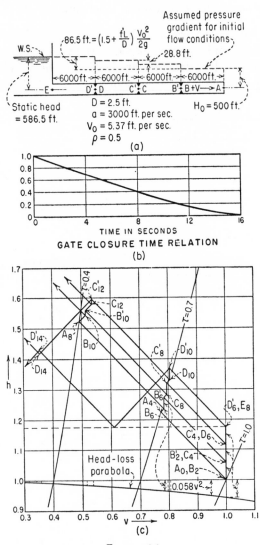

Figure 66

57. Losses concentrated at several points along pipe[3]

If a closer approximation to the effect of the hydraulic losses is required, a number of hypothetical obstructions at various locations along the pipe line are used to replace the actual losses in the pipe line. For example, consider the pipe line shown in Figure 66a and the gate closure time relation in Figure 66b. For this installation $h_f = 0.174v^2$. If the total head loss is divided evenly at three equidistant points along the pipe line, the loss at each obstruction is $0.058v^2$. This is shown by the head-loss parabola in Figure 66c together with the graphical solution. In this solution a correction is made for the head loss at each obstruction. For example, B_t and B_t' are located by trial and error on the same vertical line with the distance between them equal to the head loss shown directly below on the head-loss parabola. This method of approximating the effect of the hydraulic losses at a number of obstructions along the pipe is also applicable for pump discharge lines.

[3] See Reference 4.

XIV

Waterhammer Analysis for Compound Pipes

58. Basic equations[1]

The graphical method of waterhammer analysis used in the preceding chapters was applied to individual pipe lines without branch connections. The method was used for uniform pipe lines and also for pipe lines with stepwise changes in the diameter or

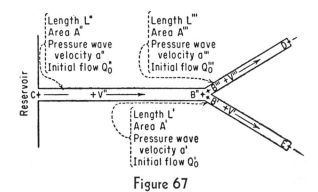

Figure 67

wave velocity along the length. By introducing the relations for the pressure ratios and the continuity of flow at the junction of a number of pipes, a method for determining the waterhammer effects for any system of compound piping is now developed.

Whenever three pipes meet at a junction as shown in Figure 67 and the velocity head and the hydraulic losses are neglected,

$$h_{B't} = h_{B''t} = h_{B'''t,} \tag{53}$$

[1] See Reference 5.

The requirement for the continuity of flow at the junction is

$$A''V_{B''t} = A'''V_{B'''t} + A'V_{B't}.$$ (54)

If this equation is divided through by $A''V_{B''0}$,

$$\frac{V_{B''t}}{V_{B''0}} = \frac{A'''V_{B'''t}}{A''V_{B''0}} + \frac{A'V_{B't}}{A''V_{B''0}}.$$

The terms on the right-hand side of the equation are now defined as follows:

$$\bar{v}_{B'''t} = \frac{A'''V_{B'''t}}{A''V_{B''0}} = \frac{A'''V_{B'''t}}{Q_0''}; \qquad \bar{v}_{B't} = \frac{A'V_{B't}}{A''V_{B''0}} = \frac{A'V_{B't}}{Q_0''}.$$

This arbitrary definition of the velocity ratios $\bar{v}_{B'''t}$ and $\bar{v}_{B't}$ simplifies the graphical representation of the waterhammer equations for compound pipes. The requirement for the continuity of flow at the junction is then

$$v_{B''t} = \bar{v}_{B'''t} + \bar{v}_{B't}.$$ (55)

The conjugate waterhammer equation for an F type wave between B' and E is

$$H_{B't_1} - H_{Et_2} = \frac{a'}{g}(V_{B't_1} - V_{Et_2}),$$

where

$$t_2 - t_1 = \frac{L'}{a'}.$$

This equation may be written in the following form:

$$h_{B't_1} - h_{Et_2} = 2\bar{\rho}'(\bar{v}_{B't_1} - \bar{v}_{Et_2}),$$ (56A)

where

$$\bar{\rho}' = \frac{a'Q_0''}{2gH_0A'}.$$

The equation for an f type wave between E and B' is

$$h_{Et_3} - h_{B't_4} = -2\bar{\rho}'(\bar{v}_{Et_3} - \bar{v}_{B't_4}).$$ (56B)

A similar development from the conjugate waterhammer equation in pipe line $B''C$ leads to

$$\rho'' = \frac{a''Q_0''}{2gH_0A''} = \frac{a''V_0''}{2gH_0}$$

and for the pipe line $B'''D$,

$$\bar{\rho}''' = \frac{a'''Q_0''}{2gH_0A'''}.$$

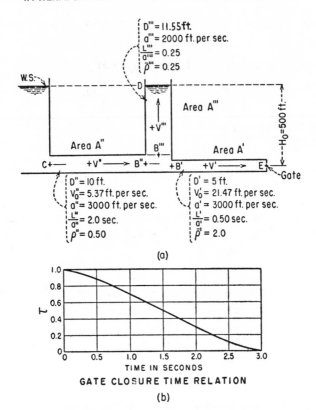

(a)

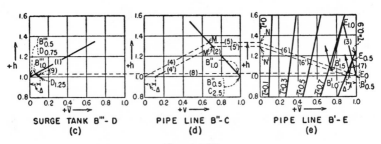

GATE CLOSURE TIME RELATION

(b)

SURGE TANK B'''- D
(c)

PIPE LINE B''-C
(d)

PIPE LINE B'-E
(e)

Figure 68

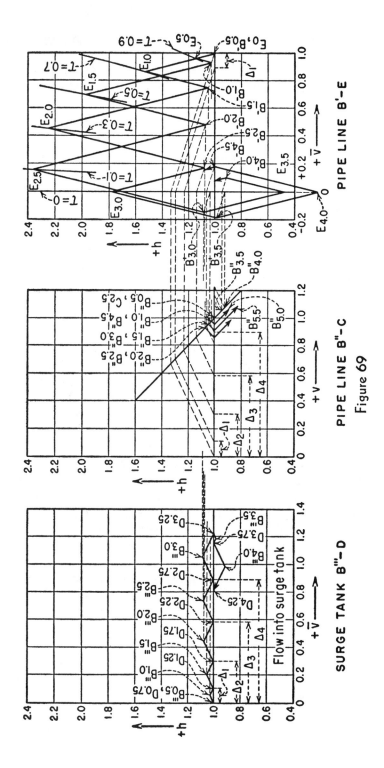

Figure 69

PIPE LINE B'-E

PIPE LINE B"-C

SURGE TANK B"'-D

It is noted that $\bar{\rho}'$ and $\bar{\rho}'''$ are not true pipe line constants for their respective pipes but are similar in form to the pipe line constants. These equations are now used for several types of compound pipe systems.

59. Pipe line with a surge tank

Consider the pipe system with a surge tank shown in Figure 68a and the gate closure time shown in Figure 68b. During the gate closure time the change in level of the water surface in the surge tank is small and is neglected. However, at a considerable time later the water level in the surge tank will rise slowly to a maximum value as the velocity of water in the pipe line $B''C$ is reduced to zero. This slow surge phenomena is discussed in Chapter XVII.

Prior to the gate movement no water is flowing into or out of the surge tank. Hence, E_0, B_0', B_0'', and C_0 are located at $h = 1$, $v = 1$, while B_0''' and D_0 are located at $h = 1$, $v = 0$. Moreover, because of the respective wave travel times $B_{0.5}'$, $B_{0.5}''$, and $C_{2.5}$ are also located at $h = 1$, $v = 1$; and $B_{0.5}'''$, $D_{0.75}$ are located at $h = 1$, $v = 0$. The complete graphical solution of the problem is shown in Figure 69, and the detailed construction is shown in Figures 68c, d, and e. The solution utilizes the conjugate waterhammer equations for the three pipe sections, the head ratios and the continuity of flow at the junction and the manner of gate closure. The solution consists of three h-v coordinate systems, one for each of the components of the pipe line with $h = 1$ on the same horizontal line. The grid system (e) on the right-hand side of Figure 68 applies for the pipe line $B'E$ adjacent to the control gate, and contains parabolas corresponding to the discharge through the gate. The grid system (d) at the center of the diagram applies for the pipe line $B''C$ and the grid system (c) at the left-hand side of the diagram applies for the surge tank or pipe section $B'''D$. The detailed solution is obtained as follows: Line (1) having a slope of $2\bar{\rho}''' = 0.5$ is set off from $D_{0.75}$ on grid (c). Similarly, the line (2) with slope $-2\bar{\rho}'' = -1$ is set off from $B_{0.5}''$ on grid (d) and the line (3) with slope $-2\bar{\rho}' = -4$ is set off from $B_{0.5}'$ on grid (e). Lines (4, 5, and 6) are construction lines. Line (4) is parallel to line (1) and starts from $h = 1$, $v = 0$ on grid (d) until it intersects with the line (2) at the point M. Line (5) is the horizontal line passing through M until it intersects the vertical axis of grid (e) at point N. Line (6) connects point N and $B'_{0.5}$ on grid (e). Since no pressure wave returns to the gate until 1 second has elapsed, line (3) is extended until it intersects the parabola at $E_{1.0}$ corresponding to the gate opening of 1 second. The location of $E_{0.5}$ is determined in a similar manner. Line (7) which originates at $E_{0.5}$ and has a slope of $+2\bar{\rho}'$ is then drawn. The intersection of lines (6) and (7) locates B'_1. Since $h_{B'_t} = h_{B''_t} = h_{B'''_t}$ a horizontal line (8) is drawn through B'_1. The intersection of (8) and (2) determines B''_1 and that of (1) and (8) determines B'''_1. This construction satisfies the condition of the continuity of flow at the junction as defined by Equation (55). From B'''_1 line (9) with slope $-2\bar{\rho}''' = 0.5$ is drawn to intersect the line $h = 1$ of grid (c), thus establishing $D_{1.25}$. The value Δ corresponding to the horizontal distance from $D_{0.75}$ to $D_{1.25}$ is next plotted on grid (d) along the line $h = 1$ and line (4') is drawn from the point just established parallel to line (4). A similar procedure is followed for the remainder of the graphical solution as shown in Figure 69.

60. Pipe line with a dead-end branch connection

Consider the pipe line installation shown in Figure 70a and the gate closure shown in Figure 70b. The graphical waterhammer analysis for this installation is shown in Figures 70c, d, and e. This solution is similar to that shown in the preceding section with the exception that instead of the pressure ratio remaining constant, the velocity ratio $v = 0$ remains constant at D, the dead end.

61. Compound pipe system with two control gates

Consider the pipe line system shown in Figure 71a. In this system the control gates are assumed to start their closures simultaneously as shown in Figure 71b. Two sets of parabolas are used to accommodate the variable flow at each control gate. The starting point in the graphical solution is located from the initial flow ratios in the branch pipes, and the solution is completed as shown in the figure.

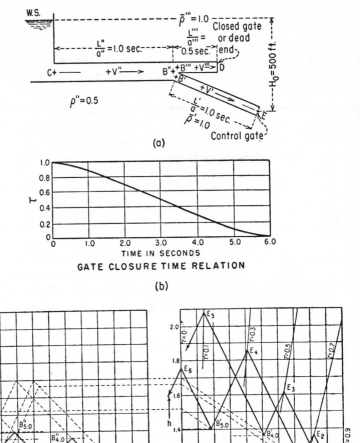

Figure 70

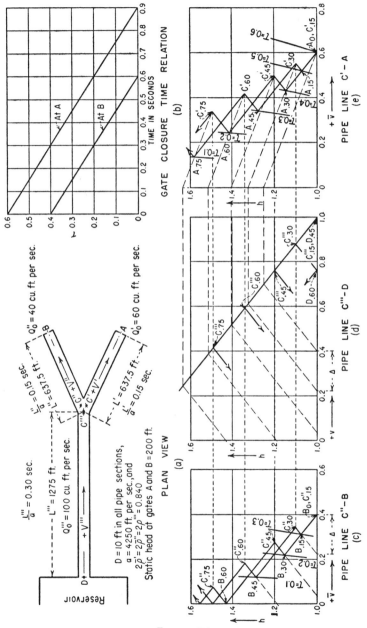

Figure 71

62. Summary

In the graphical waterhammer analysis for compound pipes one h-v grid is assigned to each pipe branch in the system. By reserving the center grid for the main or header pipe, it is possible to combine the characteristics of one of the branch pipes with the main pipe and thus enter the third grid in such a way that the analysis of all components is carried out simultaneously. This type of graphical analysis was made possible by the arbitrary definition of $\bar{v}$ and is applicable for a compound pipe system consisting of any number of pipes. The method is applicable for compound pipe systems used in pumping plants. It can also be readily adapted to accommodate the effect of the hydraulic losses or restricting orifices which may be present at any point in the system.

X V

Approximate Methods
of Graphical Waterhammer Analysis

63. Equivalent uniform pipe approximation[1]

When there are numerous changes in the cross-sectional area or wave velocity along the pipe line, the number of sloping lines in the graphical solution becomes so numerous and so close to each other that a graphical waterhammer solution by the methods described above is impractical. For example, such a condition occurs in the waterhammer solution for a pipe line with numerous changes in the thickness along the length of the pipe as the profile of the line changes. In order to obtain a satisfactory waterhammer solution for pipe lines of this type with a minimum of effort, a useful approximation can be employed which reduces the actual pipe line to an approximately equivalent uniform pipe line. When the conjugate waterhammer equations are utilized for the end points of each section of uniform pipe, the wave travel time for each section of pipe is used. In order to account for the speed of the waterhammer waves in the actual pipe, the wave travel time of the equivalent uniform pipe is taken as the sum of the wave travel times for the various pipe sections in the actual pipe line, that is,

$$\frac{L}{a} = \left(\frac{L_1}{a_1} + \frac{L_2}{a_2} + \frac{L_3}{a_3} + \ldots + \frac{L_n}{a_n} \right) = \sum \left(\frac{L_n}{a_n} \right). \qquad (57)$$

The changes in the cross-sectional area along the pipe are partially accounted for by using the relation given by Equation (6) in Chapter I for the equivalent uniform pipe based on the rigid water column theory; that is,

[1] See Reference 36.

115

$$\frac{L}{A} = \left(\frac{L_1}{A_1} + \frac{L_2}{A_2} + \frac{L_3}{A_3} + \ldots + \frac{L_n}{A_n}\right) = \Sigma\left(\frac{L_n}{A_n}\right). \qquad (58)$$

It is noted that this approximation does not include the effect of the partial wave reflections which occur at changes in the cross-sectional area or wave velocity. An approximate value for the pipe line constant for the equivalent uniform pipe line is then

$$\rho_a = \frac{Q_0\Sigma\,(L_n/A_n)}{2gH_0\Sigma\,(L_n/a_n)}. \qquad (59)$$

To illustrate the use of an equivalent uniform pipe line approximation, consider the pipe line and gate closure shown in Figures 32a and b. The value of ρ_a for the equivalent uniform pipe line which is used to replace the actual pipe line is

$$\rho_a = \frac{702.5\left(\dfrac{1800}{78.5} + \dfrac{1500}{130.9}\right)}{(2)(32.2)(500)(1)} = 0.75.$$

This equivalent uniform pipe line is shown in Figure 72a for which the graphical waterhammer solution is shown in Figure 72c. A comparison of the results using the equivalent pipe method with the more accurate method shown in Figure 32 shows that the maximum head rises at the gate and mid-length of the pipe as computed by the equivalent pipe method are slightly higher. This would be expected since the approximation neglects the effect of the wave reflections at the change in section along the pipe line. In general, this approximation gives satisfactory results when the physical discontinuities are minor in nature, such as changes in the pipe shell thickness and small changes in the cross-sectional area. The method is of course applicable to pump discharge lines as well as pipe lines involving gate operation.

64. Pipe line with surge tank

Consider the pipe line with a surge tank shown in Figure 73a and the gate closure shown in Figure 73b. This is the same installation as that shown in Figure 68. When a pressure wave from the control gate reaches the junction at B, the wave reflection factor and magnitude of the reflected wave which returns to the gate can be computed from Equation (27b). The wave re-

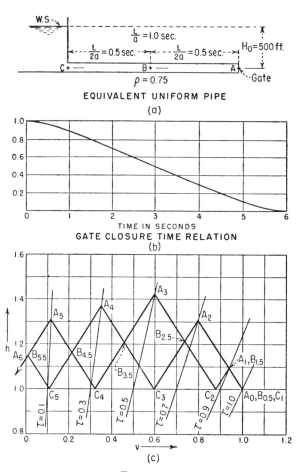

EQUIVALENT UNIFORM PIPE

(a)

GATE CLOSURE TIME RELATION

(b)

(c)

Figure 72

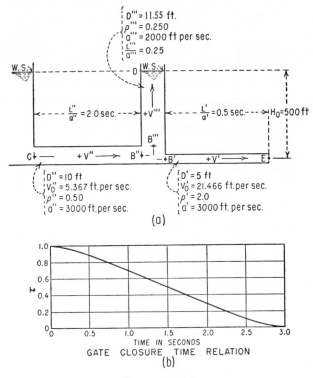

(a)

(b)

Figure 73a, b

flection factor is 0.88 for pipe line $B'E$ when all three pipes at the junction are considered. If pipe line $B''C$ is entirely neglected at the junction, the wave reflection factor for pipe line $B'E$ is 0.85. Thus a satisfactory approximation of the waterhammer effects in pipe line $B'E$ may be obtained by neglecting the presence of the pipe line $B''C$ and by considering the pipe line $B'E$ to be directly connected to the surge tank. The waterhammer solution for such an equivalent pipe line is shown in Figure 73c. A comparison between this approximate solution with the more accurate solution shown in Figure 68 indicates the approximation to be a very satisfactory one.

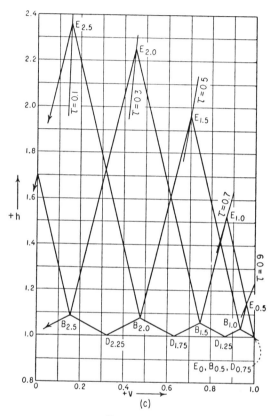

Figure 73c

XVI

Discharge Characteristics of Gates
and Valves

65. Control gates

In the solution of waterhammer problems for pipe lines involving gate operation, it was assumed that the variation in the effective area of the gate as a function of time was known from other considerations. In order to determine this gate factor, the flow characteristics of various types of gates and valves in common use will now be considered. At the present time available test data on the flow through partially open control gates are very limited. In order to determine these flow characteristics, the open area of the gate normal to the axis of the pipe was first computed, and the effective area of the gate was then determined by multiplying the open area by a suitable coefficient of discharge for the particular gate opening. Figure 74 shows the flow characteristics obtained in this manner for a typical butterfly valve, disc gate valve, ring-follower gate, and a plug valve.

66. Turbine wicket gates

The discharge through the turbine wicket gates as determined from actual tests in the field are shown in Figure 75 for a 10,500- and 150,000-horsepower unit. When the rate of closure of any of these control gates or valves is known, the variation in the effective area of the gate as a function of time can be determined. This permits the completion of the waterhammer solution by the graphical methods described above.

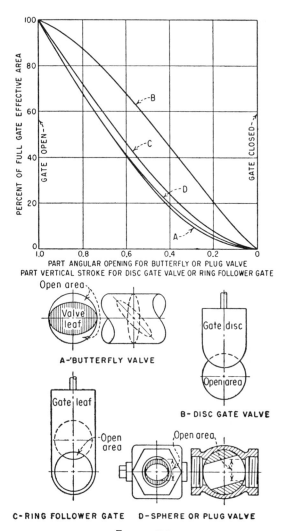

Figure 74

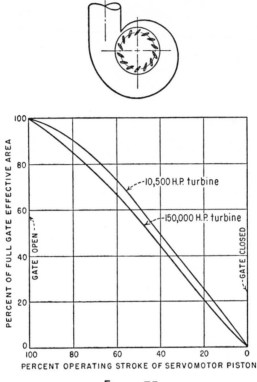

Figure 75

XVII

Surge Tanks

67. Operation

A surge tank is often used at a power or pumping plant to control the pressure changes resulting from rapid changes in the flow. For example, when the turbine gates are closed at a power plant which is supplied by a long penstock, the water surface in the surge tank rises slowly above the original running level as the kinetic energy of the rejected flow is converted into potential energy. Such a conversion of energy reduces the rate of change of flow and the waterhammer in the penstock between the forebay and surge tank. Similarly, upon an opening movement of the turbine gates, energy is provided by the surge tank for the immediate demand of the turbine. This action reduces the waterhammer effects in the long penstock and assists the turbine to pick up its increased load more rapidly.

At a pumping plant with a long discharge line, a surge tank can also be used to effectively control the pressure changes in the discharge line resulting from the shutdown or starting up of a pump. For example, following the sudden shutdown of a pump, the surge tank provides energy to reduce the rate of change of flow and the waterhammer in the discharge line. Upon starting a pump, most of the initial flow from the pump enters the surge tank and this action reduces the waterhammer effects in the long discharge line.

In order to accomplish its mission most effectively, the surge tank dimensions and location are based on the following considerations:

(a) At a power plant where the turbine output is controlled by a governor, the surge tank must have sufficient cross-sectional area to prevent unstable action. In the event the area of the tank is too small, a load change on the turbine will cause continuous oscillations of the water level in the surge tank, possibly with increasing amplitude. This problem of surge tank instability is outside the scope of this treatment.[1] In addition, the cross-sectional area of a surge tank at a power plant should be large enough that the magnitude of the surges will be small during normal load changes on the turbine. Otherwise, turbine speed regulation will be difficult or impossible.

(b) The surge tank should be located as close to the power or pumping plant as possible.

(c) The surge tank should be of sufficient height to prevent overflow for all conditions of operation unless an overflow spillway is provided.

(d) The bottom of the surge tank should be low enough that during its operation the tank will not drain and admit air into the turbine penstock or pump discharge line.

On high-head plants, where from other considerations it is necessary to place the surge tank at a considerable distance from the power or pumping plant, the farther the surge tank is away from the plant the less effective it will be. At such installations the waterhammer effects in the length of pipe between the plant and the surge tank should be investigated by the methods described in either Chapter XIV or Chapter XV.

68. Analysis neglecting hydraulic losses

Consider the simple surge tank installation shown in Figure 76 where the initial flow through the control gate is cut off rapidly. It is desired to find the maximum upsurge in the surge tank and the time at which this upsurge occurs. In order to present

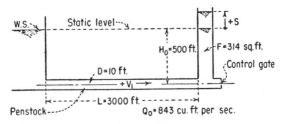

Figure 76

[1] See Reference 44.

the phenomena in its most elementary form, the hydraulic losses and the velocity head in the pipe line are initially neglected. Moreover, the rigid water column theory of waterhammer is utilized since the effect on the upsurge of the stretching of the pipe walls and the compressibility of the water due to an increase in pressure is negligible.

Prior to the gate closure, the mass of water which is moving in the penstock is LAw/g. Upon gate closure the unbalanced force acting on this water column is wAS. From Newton's second law of motion the deceleration of the water column in the penstock is

$$-\frac{dV_1}{dt} = \frac{gS}{L}. \tag{60}$$

From the condition of continuity of flow following complete gate closure, the flow of water into the surge tank is the same as that out of the penstock, that is,

$$F\frac{dS}{dt} = AV_1. \tag{61}$$

The simultaneous solution of Equations (60) and (61) is performed with the following boundary conditions: When $t = 0$, $S = 0$ and $dS/dt = Q_0/F$.

Then
$$S = \frac{Q_0}{F}\sqrt{\frac{FL}{Ag}}\sin\sqrt{\frac{Ag}{FL}}\,t, \tag{62}$$

from which
$$S_{max} = \frac{Q_0}{F}\sqrt{\frac{FL}{Ag}}, \tag{63}$$

and the time required to reach the maximum upsurge is

$$T = \frac{\pi}{2}\sqrt{\frac{FL}{Ag}}. \tag{64}$$

For the installation shown in Figure 76 the maximum upsurge in the surge tank above the static level due to the gate closure is computed to be 51.8 feet and the time required to reach this upsurge is 30.3 seconds.

69. Analysis including hydraulic losses and throttling

Consider the surge tank system shown in Figure 77 where the positive directions of flow and surge are designated. The magnitude of the surge in the tank with the friction effects included will now be determined. The head tending to accelerate the water in the pipe line in the direction of the positive velocity V_1 is

$$H_a = -S \pm c_1 V_1^2 \pm c_2 V_2^2, \tag{65}$$

where the signs of the last two terms depend on the direction of V_1 and V_2. In this equation c_1 is a constant such that $c_1 V_1 = H_{f_1}$

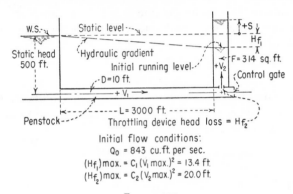

Initial flow conditions:
$Q_0 = 843$ cu.ft. per sec.
(H_{f_1})max. $= C_1 (V_1$ max.$)^2 = 13.4$ ft.
(H_{f_2})max. $= C_2 (V_2$ max.$)^2 = 20.0$ ft.

Figure 77

and represents the sum of the entrance loss, pipe line friction loss, and velocity head in the pipe line. Then c_2 is a constant such that $c_2 V_2^2 = H_{f_2}$ and represents the throttling loss for the flow into or out of the surge tank. The following tabulation gives H_a for four possible cases:

(a) Case 1 (upsurge caused by turbine shutdown), $V_1 > 0$, $V_2 > 0$,

$$H_a = -S - c_1 V_1^2 - c_2 V_2^2. \tag{65A}$$

(b) Case 2 (downsurge caused by starting up turbine), $V_1 > 0$, $V_2 < 0$.

$$H_a = -S - c_1 V_1^2 + c_2 V_2^2. \tag{65B}$$

(c) Case 3 (downsurge caused by pump shutdown), $V_1 < 0$, $V_2 < 0$.

$$H_a = -S + c_1 V_1^2 + c_2 V_2^2. \tag{65C}$$

(d) Case 4 (upsurge caused by starting pump), $V_1 < 0$, $V_2 > 0$.

$$H_a = -S + c_1 V_1^2 - c_2 V_2^2. \tag{65D}$$

The mass of fluid in the pipe line being accelerated is wAL/g and its acceleration at any time is dV_1/dt. Then from Newton's second law of motion

$$\frac{dV_1}{dt} = \frac{g}{L} H_a.$$ (66)

For continuity of flow

$$V_2 = \frac{AV_1 - Q}{A_2},$$ (67)

and

$$\frac{dS}{dt} = \frac{AV_1 - Q}{F}.$$ (68)

By substituting Equation (65) into (66) and using (67) and (68) to eliminate V_1 and V_2, a differential equation is obtained in S and t. By suitable changes in variable this equation reduces to the following form:

$$\frac{d^2S_2}{dt_1^2} \pm \frac{1}{2}\left(\frac{dS_2}{dt_1}\right)^2 + 2b\left(\frac{dS_2}{dt_1}\right) + S_2 = 0.$$ (69)

In this equation

$$b = \pm\frac{c_1 Q}{A}\sqrt{\frac{Fg}{AL}} = \pm\frac{H_{f_1}}{Q}\sqrt{\frac{Fg}{(L/A)}}.$$

Now S_2 is a function of S, and t_1 is a function of t. For example, Case 1 for turbine shutdown reduces to the following differential equation:

$$\frac{d^2S}{dt^2} + \frac{Fg}{AL}\left(c_1 + c_2\frac{A}{A_2^2}\right)\left(\frac{dS}{dt}\right)^2 + 2c_1\frac{Qg}{AL}\frac{dS}{dt}$$
$$+ \frac{Ag}{FL}\left(S + c_1\frac{Q^2}{A^2}\right) = 0.$$ (70)

The substitutions

$$S = S_1 - c_1\frac{Q^2}{A^2},$$

$$S_1 = \frac{ALS_2}{2Fg[c_1 + c_2(A^2/A_2^2)]}$$

and

$$t = \sqrt{\frac{FL}{Ag}}\, t_1,$$

reduce Equation (70) to one form of Equation (69). The solutions[2] of Equation (69) for the four special cases of turbine and

[2] See Reference 19.

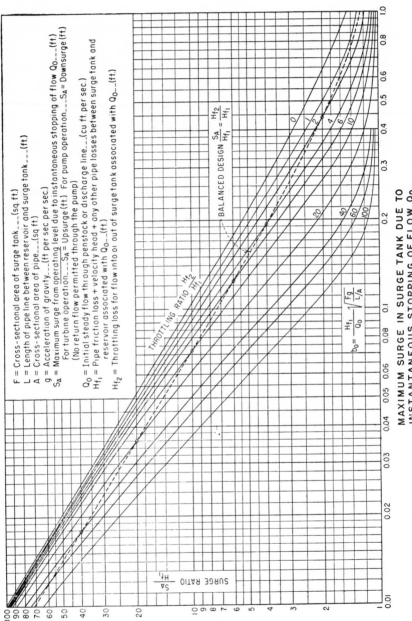

F = Cross-sectional area of surge tank___(sq.ft.)
L = Length of pipe line between reservoir and surge tank___(ft.)
A = Cross-sectional area of pipe___(sq ft)
g = Acceleration of gravity___(ft per sec per sec.)
S_A = Maximum surge from operating level due to instantaneous stopping of flow Q_0___(ft.)
 For turbine operation___S_A = Upsurge (ft.) For pump operation___S_A = Downsurge (ft.)
 (No return flow permitted through the pump)
Q_0 = Initial steady flow through penstock or discharge line___(cu ft per sec.)
H_{f_1} = Pipe friction loss + velocity head + any other pipe losses between surge tank and
 reservoir associated with Q_0___(ft.)
H_{f_2} = Throttling loss for flow into or out of surge tank associated with Q_0___(ft.)

BALANCED DESIGN $\dfrac{S_A}{H_{f_1}} = \dfrac{H_{f_2}}{H_{f_1}}$

THROTTLING RATIO $\dfrac{H_{f_2}}{H_{f_1}}$

$b_0 = \dfrac{H_{f_1}}{Q_0}\sqrt{\dfrac{Fg}{L/A}}$

SURGE RATIO $\dfrac{S_A}{H_{f_1}}$

MAXIMUM SURGE IN SURGE TANK DUE TO
INSTANTANEOUS STOPPING OF FLOW Q_0

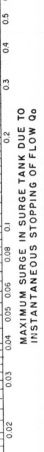

Figure 78

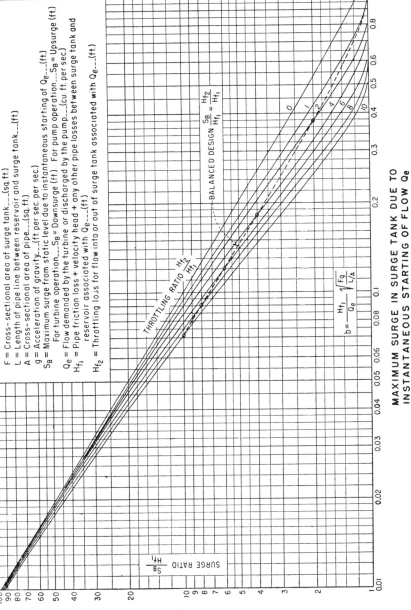

Figure 79

pump operation are shown in Figures 78 and 79. In these figures either the initial or final flow through the pump or turbine is zero. These figures are plotted in terms of the parameter b_0 or b with the ratios

$$\frac{S_A}{H_{f_1}}, \quad \text{or} \quad \frac{S_B}{H_{f_1}} \quad \text{and} \quad \frac{H_{f_2}}{H_{f_1}}.$$

Figure 78 is used to determine the surge resulting from an instantaneous stopping of the complete flow at either a turbine or pump installation, while Figure 79 is used to determine the surge caused by the instantaneous starting of the flow at either a turbine or pump installation. The broken curve is used for balanced design, where the maximum surge S_B or S_A equals the throttling loss H_{f_1}.

70. Example

To illustrate the use of the charts consider the surge tank installation shown in Figure 77. At this installation a flow of 843 cubic feet per second is shut off rapidly. For the given throttling ratio of $H_{f_2}/H_{f_1} = 1.49$ and $b_0 = 0.259$, the upsurge S_A above the running level as determined from the charts is $(3.5)(13.4) = 46.9$ feet. The upsurge S above the static level as shown in Figure 77 is then $46.9 - 13.4 = 33.5$ feet. Surge values can also be determined in a similar manner from the charts due to the starting of turbines at a power plant or for stopping or starting the pumps at a pumping plant.

XVIII

Air Chambers at Pumping Plants

71. Operation

If a power failure occurs at the motors of the pumps which supply water to a long discharge line, the initial negative surge wave may cause water column separation to occur at the high points in the discharge line which are near the hydraulic gradient.

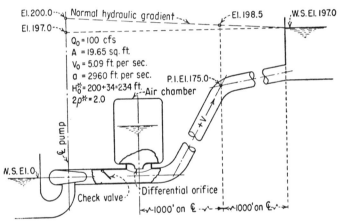

Figure 80

Whenever possible, this condition should be avoided because of the high pressures created when the water columns rejoin. A device which can effectively control the pressure surges in a long pump discharge line is an air chamber as shown in Figure 80. The lower portion of the chamber contains water, while the upper portion contains compressed air. When power failure occurs, the head developed by the pump and the flow decrease rapidly. The compressed air in the chamber then forces water out of the bottom of the chamber into the discharge line and minimizes the

131

velocity changes and waterhammer effects in the discharge line. As the pump speed is reduced to the point where it cannot deliver water against the existing head, the check valve at the discharge side of the pump closes, and the pump comes slowly to a stop. The water in the discharge line then comes to rest, reverses, and flows back into the chamber. As the reverse flow enters the chamber, the air volume decreases, and a head rise above the normal pumping head occurs in the discharge line.

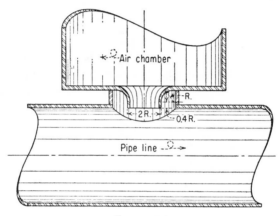

Figure 81

Air chambers at pumping plants can usually be made smaller than open surge tanks which are designed for the same purpose. Moreover, they do not have to be placed in an upright position. However, in order to be effective, chambers must be kept supplied with small amounts of compressed air to replace that which dissolves in the water. In order for a chamber to be most effective, it is necessary to throttle the reverse flow of water from the discharge line into the chamber, while very little throttling is provided for the flow out of the chamber. One device for accomplishing this is a differential orifice of the type shown in Figure 81.[1] When tested in the laboratory this particular orifice was found to give 2.5 times as much head loss for return flow into the air chamber as for flow out of the chamber.

---

[1] See Reference 9.

72. Basic considerations

Following a power interruption at the pump motor, the pressure head at the discharge side of the pump is initially maintained by the air chamber, while the pump speed and discharge fall off rapidly. This causes the check valve to close very soon after power failure. Hence it can be assumed that the check valve closes simultaneously with power failure, and that thereafter all the flow from the discharge line is from or into the chamber. This assumption eliminates the pump characteristics from the water-hammer computations but introduces an abrupt pressure wave corresponding to the instantaneous head drop across the throttling orifice at the base of the chamber.

During the transient conditions the air in the chamber initially expands as the head drops in the discharge line and later compresses as the head in the discharge line increases. In the following analysis the pressure-volume changes for the air in the chamber are taken midway between adiabatic and isothermal expansion, that is

$$H^* C^{1.2} = H_0^* C_0^{1.2} = \text{constant}. \tag{71}$$

This is written in the following form:

$$h^* c^{1.2} = 1, \tag{72}$$

where $h^* = H^*/H_0^*$ and $c = C/C_0$. The volume of air in the chamber at any time t_2 in terms of the volume at a previous time t_1 is

$$C_{t_2} = C_{t_1} - A \int_{t_1}^{t_2} V \, dt. \tag{73}$$

For small time intervals the variation in V may be assumed to be linear, and the volume of air in the chamber is then

$$C_{t_2} = C_{t_1} - \frac{A(V_{t_1} + V_{t_2})\Delta t}{2}, \tag{74}$$

where the time interval $\Delta t = t_2 - t_1$. In order to use Equation (74) with the graphical waterhammer solution, it is necessary to choose Δt as a fraction of the wave travel time in the discharge line, that is, $\Delta t = \delta(L/a)$. Then,

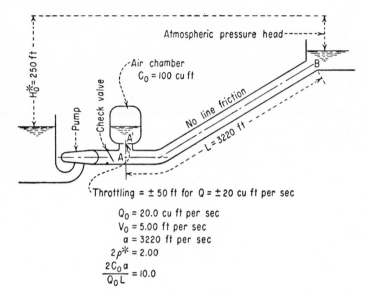

Throttling = ± 50 ft for Q = ± 20 cu ft per sec

$Q_0 = 20.0$ cu ft per sec
$V_0 = 5.00$ ft per sec
$a = 3220$ ft per sec
$2\rho^* = 2.00$
$\dfrac{2C_0 a}{Q_0 L} = 10.0$

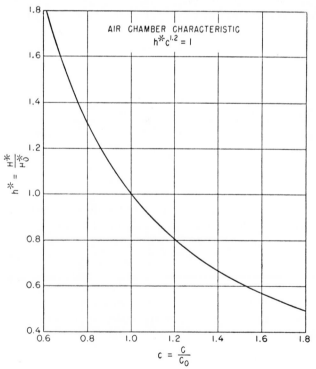

Figure 82a, b

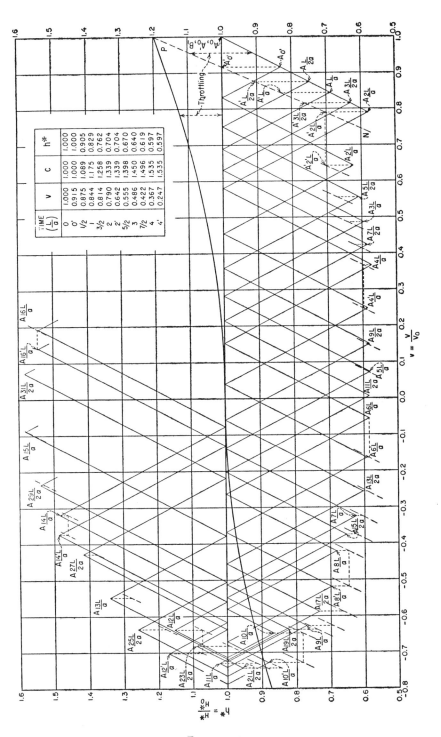

Figure 82c

$$\frac{C_{t_2}}{C_0} = \frac{C_{t_1}}{C_0} - \frac{A(V_{t_1} + V_{t_2})Q_0 L \delta}{2C_0 V_0 A a},$$

or
$$c_{t_2} = c_{t_1} - \frac{(v_{t_1} + v_{t_2})\delta}{2C_0 a/Q_0 L}. \tag{75}$$

Since the air volume changes in the chamber are defined in terms of absolute pressures, it is preferable to define the pipe line characteristic in terms of absolute pressure heads, that is,

$$\rho^* = \frac{a V_0}{2g H_0^*}. \tag{76}$$

The head changes in the discharge line are then defined by the conjugate waterhammer Equations (51A) and (51B) where ρ is replaced by ρ^*.

73. Graphical solution

Consider the pumping system with an air chamber shown in Figure 82a. From the data given, $2\rho^* = 2.00$ and $2C_0 a/Q_0 L = 10.0$. For $\delta = \frac{1}{2}$, Equation (75) reduces to

$$c_{t_2} = c_{t_1} - 0.050(v_{t_1} + v_{t_2}). \tag{77}$$

The pressure-volume relationship in the chamber as defined by Equation (72) is plotted in Figure 82b. Referring now to Figure 82c, the starting point in the graphical waterhammer solution corresponding to A_0 is located at the coordinates $h^* = 1$, $v = 1$. The assumption of instantaneous check valve closure causes an abrupt change of flow in the discharge line from A_0 to $A_{0'}$. At the same instant a head drop develops across the throttling orifice as represented by the vertical line $A_{0'}A_0$. The head changes at A from time zero to $2L/a$ seconds are located on the line of slope $2\rho^*$ which passes through A_0. The head changes inside the chamber at A' from time zero to $2L/a$ seconds are located on the throttling line PN where the vertical distance between A and A' for a given flow corresponds to the throttling loss. Now $A_{0'}'$ is located at the intersection of PN with the horizontal line $h^* = 1$, and $A_{0'}$ is located directly below. The location of $A_{L/2a}$ on the line of slope $2\rho^*$ is then determined in the following manner: The approximate location is first assumed and value of $v_{L/2a}$ is read from Figure 82c. Then $c_{L/2a}$ is computed from Equation (77) and

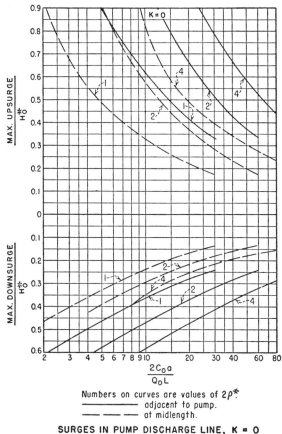

Numbers on curves are values of $2\rho^*$
————— adjacent to pump.
— — — at midlength.

SURGES IN PUMP DISCHARGE LINE, K = 0

Figure 83a

$h_{L/2a}^*$ is read from Figure 82b. The assumed value of $v_{L/2a}$ and
the computed value of $h_{L/2a}^*$ define the location of $A'_{L/2a}$, which
must fall on line PN. If it does not, the trial process is repeated
until this condition is met. This computation is then repeated
for times L/a, $3L/2a$, and $2L/a$ seconds. At time $2L/a$ seconds,
the abrupt pressure wave which was assumed to have left the
chamber at time zero returns from the discharge end of the line.
This return wave causes an instantaneous change in velocity from
$A'_{2L/a}$ to $A'_{2'L/a}$ as shown in Figure 82c. The complete solution
of the air chamber problem is then completed as shown in the
figure.

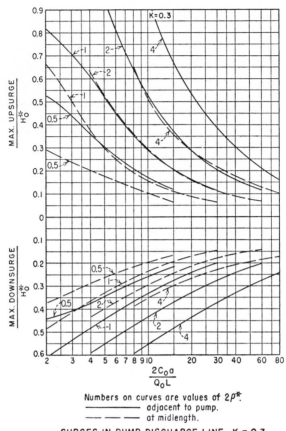

Numbers on curves are values of $2\rho^*$.
————— adjacent to pump.
— — — at midlength.

SURGES IN PUMP DISCHARGE LINE, K = 0.3

Figure 83b

74. Air chamber charts

From a study of the graphical waterhammer solution given in the preceding section it is seen that the basic parameters[2] involved in determining the waterhammer effects in a pump discharge line with an air chamber are $2\rho^*$ and $2C_0a/Q_0L$. Hence the results of a large number of air chamber solutions can be shown on a chart as shown in Figure 83. In this figure the surges in the discharge line adjacent to the chamber and at the mid-

[2] See References 2 and 15.

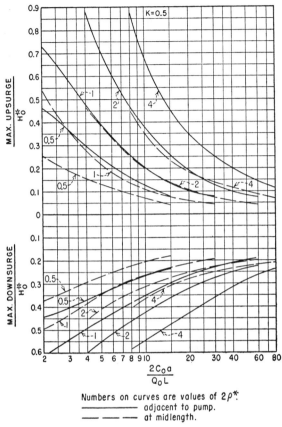

Numbers on curves are values of $2\rho^*$.
———————— adjacent to pump.
— — — — at midlength.

SURGES IN PUMP DISCHARGE LINE, K = 0.5

Figure 83c

length are plotted in terms of the basic parameters. The values shown in this figure are based on the following assumptions:

(a) The air chamber is located near the pump.

(b) The check valve at the pump closes immediately upon power failure.

(c) The pressure volume relation for the compressed air in the air chamber is $H^*C^{1.2} =$ a constant.

(d) The ratio of the total head loss for the same flow into and out of the air chamber is 2.5 to 1; KH_0^* is the sum of the hydraulic losses in the discharge line and the throttling losses at the differ-

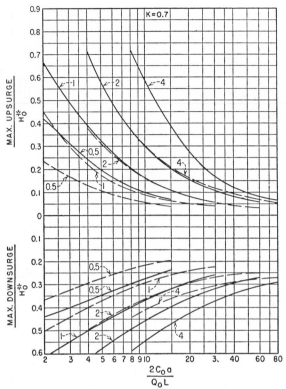

Numbers on curves are values of $2\rho^*$.
——————— adjacent to pump.
— — — — at midlength.

SURGES IN PUMP DISCHARGE LINE, K = 0.7

Figure 83d

ential orifice when a reverse flow equal to Q_0 is passing into the air chamber.

To insure that air will not enter the discharge line when the maximum downsurge is attained, the total volume of the air chamber must be greater than C', where C' is defined as follows:

$$C' = C_0 \left(\frac{H_0^*}{H_{\min}^*}\right)^{1/1.2} \approx \frac{C_0 H_0^*}{H_{\min}^*}, \qquad (78)$$

where $H_{\min}^* = H_0^*$ minus maximum downsurge adjacent to pump.

75. Example

Consider the pumping plant installation with an air chamber shown in Figure 80. It is desired to determine a chamber size such that the maximum upsurge in the discharge line adjacent to the pump will not exceed $0.43H_0^*$ and the maximum downsurge at the mid-length will not exceed $0.21H_0^*$. From the charts in Figure 83 it is found that these requirements are met by using the values $K = 0.3$ and $2C_0a/Q_0L = 21$ for which the maximum upsurge at the pump $= 0.27H_0^*$, the maximum downsurge at the mid-length $= 0.21H_0^*$, and the maximum downsurge adjacent to the pump $= 0.32H_0^*$. For this installation the pipe line friction loss for a flow Q_0 is about 3 feet. The differential orifice required at the chamber must then give a head loss for a flow of Q_0 into the chamber of $0.3 \times 234 - 3 = 67$ feet. With $2C_0a/Q_0L$ known, the initial volume of compressed air in the chamber C_0 is 709 cubic feet and the minimum volume for the whole air chamber C' as determined from Equation (78) is 1040 cubic feet.

76. Water level controls

In the previous example, the calculations for downsurge and upsurge were based on the same initial volume of air in the chamber. In an actual installation some fluctuation in the water surface level in the chamber will occur since air is constantly going into solution and the air compressor cannot maintain a fixed water level. These changes in water level in the chamber can be used to actuate the controls in the pumping plant. Two sets of control levels are usually required, namely, the upper and lower emergency levels and the compressor 'on' and 'off' levels as shown in Figure 84. When the water level in the chamber reaches either of the emergency levels, the pumping plant is automatically shut down. The volume of the air in the chamber is determined from the consideration that there must be adequate air in the chamber above the upper emergency level to control the surges in the discharge line to desirable limits, and there must also be enough water in the chamber below the lower emergency level to prevent air from entering the discharge line. In order to obtain the total

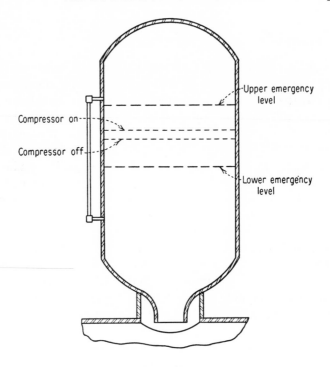

Upper emergency
level

Compressor on

Compressor off

Lower emergency
level

AIR CHAMBER CONTROL LEVELS

Figure 84

volume of the air chamber for these conditions, C_0 is computed
from the charts in Figure 83 as before and is then increased by an
amount equal to the volume of the chamber between the upper
and lower emergency levels. A new value of $H^*_{\min}$ at the base of
the chamber is then obtained from the charts. The total volume
of the chamber C' is then determined from Equation (78), using
the new values of $H^*_{\min}$ and C_0.

References

1. ALLIEVI, L., *Theory of Waterhammer*, translated by E. E. Halmos, printed by Riccardo Garoni, Rome, Italy, 1925.

2. ALLIEVI, L., "Air Chambers for Discharge Pipes," *Transactions ASME*, Vol. 59, Paper Hyd-59-7, November 1937, pp. 651–659.

3. ANGUS, R. W., "Simple Graphical Solution for Pressure Rise in Pipes and Pump Discharge Lines," *The Journal of the Engineering Institute of Canada*, February, 1935, pp. 72–81.

4. ANGUS, R. W., "Waterhammer in Pipes, Including Those Supplied by Centrifugal Pumps: Graphical Treatment," *Bulletin 152*, University of Toronto Press, 1938.

5. ANGUS, R. W., "Waterhammer Pressures in Compound and Branched Pipes," *Proceedings ASCE*, No. 2024, January 1938, pp. 340–401.

6. ANGUS, R. W., "Air Chambers and Valves in Relation to Waterhammer," *Transactions ASME*, Vol. 59, Paper Hyd-59-8, November, 1937, pp. 661–668.

7. BERGERON, L., "Etude des variations de regime dans les conduites d'eau: Solution graphique generale," *Revue generale de l'hydraulique*, Paris, Vol. 1, 1935, pp. 12–69.

8. BERGERON, L., *Du coup de belier en hydraulique au coup de foudre en electricite*, Dunod, Paris, 1950.

9. BERGERON, L., Discussion of L. Allievi's paper, "Air Chambers for Discharge Pipes," *Transactions ASME*, Vol. 61, July, 1939, pp. 441–445.

10. BILLINGS, A. W. K., DODKIN, O. H., KNAPP, F., and SANTOS, A., JR., "High-Head Penstock Design," *Symposium on Waterhammer, ASME—ASCE*, 1933, pp. 29–61.

11. CALAME, J., and GADEN, D., *Theorie des chambres d'equilibre*, Gauthur-Villars, Paris, 1926.

12. CRAWFORD, C. C., "Curves for the Quick Estimation of Transient Hydraulic Conditions Following Failure of Electric Power to a Pumping Plant," *Thesis for M.S. Degree*, University of Colorado, 1948.

13. DAWSON, F. M., and KALINSKE, A. A., "Methods of Calculating Waterhammer Pressures," *Journal of the American Water Works Association*, Vol. 31, No. 11, November, 1939, pp. 1835–1864.

14. DURAND, W. F., *Hydraulics of Pipe Lines*, D. Van Nostrand Company, Inc., New York, 1921.

15. EVANS, W. E., and CRAWFORD, C. C., "Design Charts for Air Chambers on Pump Lines," *Transactions ASCE*, Vol. 119, No. 2710, 1954, pp. 1025–1045.

16. GIBSON, N. R., "Pressures in Penstocks Caused by the Gradual Closing of Turbine Gates," *Transactions ASCE*, Vol. 83, 1919–1920, pp. 707–775.

17. GLOVER, R. E., "Computation of Waterhammer Pressures in Compound Pipes," *Symposium on Waterhammer, ASME—ASCE*, 1933, pp. 64–69.

18. HALMOS, E. E., "Effects of Surge Tanks on the Magnitude of Waterhammer in Pipe Lines," *Symposium on Waterhammer, ASME—ASCE*, 1933, pp. 72–80.

19. JACOBSON, R. S., "Charts for Analysis of Surge Tanks in Turbine or Pump Installations," *Special Report 104*, Bureau of Reclamation, Denver, Colorado, February, 1952.

20. JAEGER, C., "Waterhammer Effects in Power Conduits," *Civil Engineering and Public Works Review*, 1948.

21. JAEGER, C., "Theory of Resonance in Pressure Conduits," *Transactions ASME*, Vol. 61, February, 1939, pp. 109–115.

22. JOHNSON, R. D., "The Differential Surge Tank," *Transactions ASCE*, Vol. 78, 1915, pp. 760–805.

23. JOHNSON, R. D., "The Surge Tank in Water Power Plants," *Transactions ASME*, Vol. 30, No. 1204, 1908, pp. 443–501.

24. JOUKOWSKY, N., "Waterhammer," Translated by Miss O. Simin, *Proceedings AWWA*, Vol. 24, 1904, pp. 341–424.

25. KERR, S. L., "Fall in Pressure in Hydraulic Turbine Penstocks Due to Acceleration of Flow," *Power*, Vol. 60, No. 7, August, 1924, pp. 266–268.

26. KERR, S. L., "New Aspects of Maximum Pressure Rise in Closed Conduits," *Transactions ASME*, Vol. 51 (1), Paper Hyd-51-3, 1929, pp. 13–30.

27. KERR, S. L., and STROWGER, E. B., "Resumé of Theory of Waterhammer in Simple Conduits," *Symposium on Waterhammer, ASME—ASCE*, 1933, pp. 15–24.

28. KESSLER, L. H., "Speed of Waterhammer Pressure Waves in Transite Pipe," *Transactions ASME*, Vol. 61, January, 1939, pp. 11–15.

29. KNAPP, R. T., "Complete Characteristics of Centrifugal Pumps and Their Use in the Prediction of Transient Behavior," *Transactions ASME*, Vol. 59, Paper Hyd-59-11, November, 1937, pp. 683–689.

30. KRUSE, O. V., Discussion of N. R. Gibson's paper, "Pressures in Penstocks Caused by the Gradual Closing of Turbine Gates," *Transactions ASCE*, Vol. 83, 1919–1920, pp. 741–747.

31. LE CONTE, J. N., "Experiments and Calculations on the Resurge Phase of Waterhammer," *Transactions ASME*, Vol. 59, Paper Hyd-59-12, November, 1937, pp. 691–694.

32. Moody, L. F., "Simplified Derivation of Waterhammer Formula," *Symposium on Waterhammer, ASME—ASCE*, 1933, pp. 25–28.

33. Parmakian, J., "Pressure Surges at Large Pump Installations," *Transactions ASME*, Vol. 75, August, 1953, pp. 995–1006.

34. Parmakian, J., "Pressure Surge Control at Tracy Pumping Plant," *Proceedings ASCE*, Vol. 79, Separate No. 361, December, 1953.

35. Peabody, R. M., "Typical Analysis of Waterhammer in a Pumping Plant of the Colorado River Aqueduct," *Transactions ASME*, Vol. 61, February, 1939, pp. 117–124.

36. Quick, R. S., "Comparison and Limitations of Various Waterhammer Theories," *Transactions ASME*, Vol. 49, No. 5a, May, 1927, pp. 524–530.

37. Rich, G. R., *Hydraulic Transients*, 1st ed., Engineering Societies Monographs, McGraw-Hill Book Co., Inc., New York, 1951. (Dover Reprint)

38. Schnyder, O., "Comparisons Between Calculated and Test Results on Waterhammer in Pumping Plant," *Transactions ASME*, Vol. 59, Paper Hyd-59-13, November, 1937, pp. 695–700.

39. Stepanoff, A. J., *Centrifugal and Axial Flow Pumps*, John Wiley & Sons, Inc., New York, 1948.

40. Strowger, E. B., "Relation of Relief-Valve and Turbine Characteristics in the Determination of Waterhammer," *Transactions ASME*, Vol. 59, Paper Hyd-59-14, November, 1937, pp. 701–705.

41. Strowger, E. B., "Waterhammer Problems in Connection with the Design of Hydroelectric Plants," *Transactions ASME*, Vol. 67, July, 1945, pp. 377–392.

42. Strowger, E. B., and Kerr, S. L., "Speed Changes of Hydraulic Turbines for Sudden Changes of Load," *Transactions ASME*, Vol. 48, No. 2009, 1926, pp. 209–262.

43. *Symposium on Waterhammer, ASME—ASCE*, 1933.

44. Thoma, D., *Beitrage zur Theorie des Wasserschlosses bei selbsttatig geregelten Turbinenanlagen*, Oldenburg, Munchen, 1910.

45. Timoshenko, S., *Strength of Materials*, 2d ed., Part 2, D. Van Nostrand Company, Inc., New York, 1941.

46. Warren, M. M., "Penstock and Surge Tank Problems," *Transactions ASCE*, Vol. 79, 1915, pp. 238–305.

47. Wood, F. M., "The Application of Heavisides Operational Calculus to the Solutions of Problems in Waterhammer," *Transactions ASME*, Vol. 59, Paper Hyd-59-15, November, 1937, pp. 707–713.

Problems

Chapter I

1. A pipe line has the following characteristics: $L = 2500$ feet, $H_0 = 150$ feet, and $D = 6$ inches.

(a) What is the maximum pressure at the control gate if the initial steady flow of 600 gallons per minute is cut off uniformly in 10 seconds?

(b) What is the factor of safety if the bursting strength of the pipe is 375 pounds per square inch? *Ans.* (a) 92 pounds per square inch, (b) 4.1.

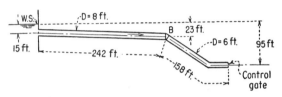

Figure 85

2. The full gate discharge for the pipe line shown in Figure 85 is 300 cubic feet per second.

(a) What is the maximum head at the control gate if one-half of the full gate discharge is cut off by a uniform gate closure in 4 seconds?

(b) What is the minimum head at the center line of the pipe at B if the control gate is opened from zero gate to full gate in 5 seconds? *Ans.* (a) 108 feet, (b) 15 feet.

3. (a) Show that the equivalent length of uniform pipe of diameter D_1 which can be used to replace the tapered tunnel section shown in Figure 86 in the waterhammer computations is $L_1 D_1/D_2$.

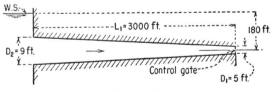

Figure 86

(b) What is the maximum head rise at the control gate if the initial flow of 250 cubic feet per second is cut off uniformly in 12 seconds? *Ans.* (b) 64 feet.

147

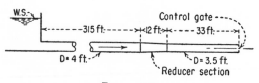

Figure 87

4. Calculate the equivalent length of uniform pipe of 42-inch diameter for the pipe line shown in Figure 87. *Ans.* 285 feet.

Chapter III

5. What is the waterhammer wave velocity in a circular conduit with rigid walls? *Ans.* 4720 feet per second.

6. (a) Compute the waterhammer wave velocity in a steel pipe 42 inches in outside diameter and ⅜ inch thick if the pipe line is anchored at one end only.

(b) What is the wave velocity if the water is replaced with crude oil whose specific gravity is 0.80 and bulk modulus is 220,000 pounds per square inch? *Ans.* (a) 3300 feet per second, (b) 3400 feet per second.

7. Compute the waterhammer wave velocity for a 95-inch inside wood-stave pipe for which the ¾-inch diameter steel bands are spaced at 5 inches and the wood staves are 3 inches thick. Assume that the pipe line is anchored at one end only. *Ans.* (a) 1720 feet per second.

8. Compute the waterhammer wave velocity in a 4-foot inside diameter reinforced concrete pipe line which is anchored against longitudinal movement throughout its length. The pipe walls consist of concrete 6 inches thick with 1-inch diameter steel reinforcement bars spaced at 12-inch centers. *Ans.* 3190 feet per second.

9. (a) Compute the waterhammer wave velocity for a steel-lined circular pressure tunnel at which $D = 10$ feet, $e = 1$ inch, $E = 30 \times 10^6$ pounds per square inch and $G = 2 \times 10^6$ pounds per square inch.

(b) If the steel liner is removed what is the waterhammer wave velocity in the tunnel? *Ans.* (a) 4440 feet per second, (b) 4400 feet per second.

Chapter IV

10. At the installation shown in Figure 88 an instantaneous closing movement of the regulating gate at A produces a positive pressure wave of 25 feet at the gate. Determine the magnitude of the pressure wave which is:

(a) Reflected back from the junction C toward the gate in pipe section CA.

(b) Transmitted to pipe sections CB, CE, and CG.

(c) Reflected back from the reservoir at E.

(d) Reflected back from the free water surface at G.

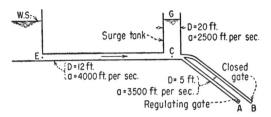

Figure 88

(e) Reflected back from the closed gate at B. *Ans.* (a) -23.3 feet, (b) $+1.7$ feet, (c) -1.7 feet, (d) -1.7 feet, (e) $+1.7$ feet.

11. Assume that at a given instant a positive pressure wave of 10-foot magnitude traveling in the direction of flow inside the pipe has just reached an open control gate. Determine the magnitude of the reflected pressure wave leaving the gate if $B = 0.25$, $H_0 = 676$ feet, $V_0 = 6.5$ feet per second, and $a = 2950$ feet per second. *Ans.* $+3.9$ feet.

Chapter V

12. A pipe line 3900 feet long has a waterhammer wave velocity of 2900 feet per second and an initial water velocity of 4.5 feet per second.

(a) What is the head rise at the control gate if the entire flow is cut off in 0.6 second?

(b) What is the farthest point along the pipe line away from the control gate at which this maximum head rise is attained? *Ans.* (a) 405 feet, (b) 3030 feet.

13. Compute the head rise for each foot per second of velocity suddenly extinguished for a pipe line carrying oil of specific gravity 0.75 and bulk modulus of 200,000 pounds per square inch. The pipe line has an inside diameter of 12 inches, a wall thickness of $\frac{1}{8}$ inch and is anchored at one end only. *Ans.* 110 feet.

14. Construct a pressure wave time history diagram similar to Figure 19 in the text for an instantaneous partial gate closure.

Chapter VI

15. As a result of a closing movement of the control gate at the pipe line shown in Figure 89, the head rise at the gate varies in the following manner:

t (seconds),	0	0.25	0.50	0.75	1	1.25	1.50	1.75	2
$(F + f)$ (feet),	0	4	10	17	25	30	32	33	33

What is the total head at B and C at $t = 1$ and $t = 1.75$ seconds? *Ans.* 142 feet and 147 feet at B, 110 feet and 113 feet at C.

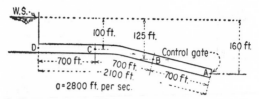

Figure 89

16. Compute the minimum head at the gate and mid-length of the pipe line shown in Figure 23 of the text for the following gate opening:

t (seconds),	0	1	2	3	4	5	6	7	8
$C_d A_g$ (square feet),	0	0.50	1.0	1.55	3.15	3.80	4.20	4.50	4.70

Use one-second time intervals in computations. *Ans.* 285 feet and 260 feet.

Chapter VII

17. A pipe line has the following characteristics: $L = 1350$ feet, $a = 3600$ feet per second, $V_0 = 3.25$ feet per second and $H_0 = 150$ feet. Compute the maximum head rise at the control gate for the following gate closure:

t (seconds),	0	0.75	1.50	2.25	3.00	3.75	4.50	5.25	6
τ,	1.00	0.975	0.925	0.85	0.80	0.65	0.50	0.35	0

Ans. 110 feet.

Chapter VIII

18. A pipe line has the following characteristics: $L = 2400$ feet, $a = 3200$ feet per second, $H_0 = 325$ feet and $V_0 = 5.5$ feet per second.

(a) Compute the maximum head rise at the control gate and one-third points in the pipe line for uniform gate closure to the half open gate position in 3 seconds.

(b) Construct a pressure time history diagram for the pressure changes at the control gate from $t = 0$ to $t = 6$ seconds. *Ans.* (a) 85 feet, 60 feet, and 30 feet.

19. Compute the maximum head at the control gate and the junction B for the pipe line shown in Figure 90 for the following gate closure:

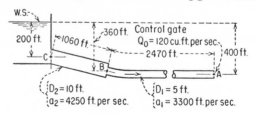

Figure 90

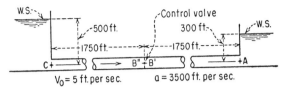

Figure 91

t (seconds),	0	0.5	1.0	1.5	2.0	2.5	3.0	3.5	4.0	4.5	5.0
τ,	1.00	0.77	0.60	0.46	0.36	0.28	0.20	0.15	0.10	0.05	0

Ans. 655 feet and 405 feet.

20. Compute the maximum head rise at B'' for the pipe line shown in Figure 91 for a uniform gate closure in 5 seconds. *Ans.* 75 feet.

21. Compute the maximum head at the gate and mid-length for the pipe line shown in Figure 92 for the following control gate and relief valve operation:

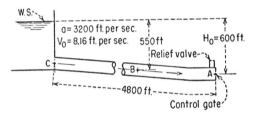

Figure 92

t (seconds),	0	1.5	3.0	4.5	6.0
τ (control gate),	1.00	0.58	0.30	0.13	0
τ (relief valve),	0	0.14	0.40	0.65	0.8

Ans. 770 feet and 705 feet.

22. Compute the minimum head at B' for the pipe line shown in Figure 93 for the following gate closure:

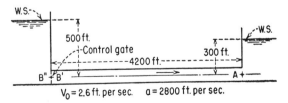

Figure 93

t (seconds),	0	1.5	3.0	4.5	6.0	7.5
τ,	1.00	0.90	0.70	0.50	0.30	0

Ans. 235 feet.

Chapter IX

23. A pipe line has the following characteristics: $L = 4800$ feet, $H_0 = 400$ feet, $a = 3200$ feet per second and $V_e = 4$ feet per second. Determine the minimum and maximum head at the control gate for the following gate opening:

t (seconds),	0	1.5	3.0	4.5	6.0
τ,	0	0.49	0.77	0.93	1.0

Ans. 190 feet and 415 feet.

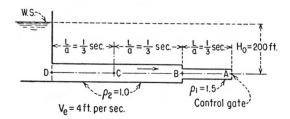

Figure 94

24. Compute the minimum head at the points A, B, and C for the pipe line shown in Figure 94 for a uniform gate opening in $5\frac{1}{3}$ seconds. *Ans.* 90 feet, 120 feet, and 150 feet.

Chapter X

25. A pipe line has the following characteristics: $L = 4250$ feet, $H_0 = 100$ feet, $a = 3200$ feet per second, and $V_0 = 3.90$ feet per second.

(a) Compute the maximum head at the control gate for a uniform gate closure in 7 seconds.

(b) Compute the minimum head at the control gate for a uniform gate opening in 9 seconds where $V_e = 3.90$ feet per second.

(c) Recompute (a) and (b) assuming a wave velocity of 4000 feet per second. *Ans.* (a) 210 feet, (b) 35 feet, (c) 210 feet and 35 feet.

Chapter XI

26. A pump installation has the following characteristics: Number and type of pumps, two single suction pumps with characteristics shown in Figure 51 of text,

WR^2 of each pump and motor, 325,000 pound feet²,
Pump speed, 327 revolutions per minute,
Rated head of pump, 186 feet,
Discharge capacity of each pump at rated head, 205 cubic feet per second,
Pump efficiency at rated head, 89.0 per cent,
Inside diameter of discharge line pipe, 11 feet,
Length of discharge line, 4800 feet,
Average wave velocity of discharge line pipe, 4000 feet per second.

Determine from a graphical waterhammer analysis the maximum rise and drop in head at the pump and mid-length of the discharge line for a simultaneous power failure at both pump motors. Use time intervals of 0.6 second in the computations and neglect hydraulic losses. *Ans.* Head rise = 95 feet and 50 feet. Head drop = 150 feet and 90 feet.

27. What is the maximum rise and drop in head at the pump and mid-length of the discharge line of Problem 26 when a power failure occurs with only one pump in operation? *Ans.* Head rise = 60 feet and 30 feet. Head drop = 125 feet and 85 feet.

Chapter XII

28. Re-solve Problem 26 assuming that there is a check valve on the discharge side of each pump which closes immediately upon a flow reversal at the pump. *Ans.* Head rise = 150 feet and 85 feet. Head drop = 150 feet and 85 feet.

29. Re-solve Problem 26 assuming that the WR^2 of the pump and motor is increased 100 per cent. *Ans.* Head rise = 60 feet and 30 feet. Head drop = 125 feet and 70 feet.

30. What is the maximum head rise in the discharge line of Problem 26 caused by the sudden starting of one pump or two pumps simultaneously with the discharge line full? *Ans.* 19 feet.

31. Re-solve Problem 26, assuming that a suction line of wave travel time $L_2/a_2 = 0.6$ second and having the same pipe line characteristic as the discharge line is added to the installation. *Ans.* Head rise = 80 feet and 45 feet. Head drop = 125 feet and 70 feet.

32. Solve Problems 26 and 27 by using the waterhammer charts in Figure 57 of the text. *Ans.* For 2-unit shutdown: Head rise = 60 feet and 30 feet. Head drop = 140 feet and 85 feet. For 1-unit shutdown: Head rise = 40 feet and 25 feet. Head drop = 115 feet and 70 feet.

Chapter XIII

33. A pipe line has the following characteristics: $L = 30,000$ feet, $D = 2.5$ feet, $V_0 = 5.37$ feet per second, $a = 3000$ feet per second, static head = 608 feet, and hydraulic losses = 108 feet. Compute the maximum head at the

control gate for a uniform gate closure in one minute for the following cases:
  (a) Hydraulic losses concentrated at the intake.
  (b) Hydraulic losses concentrated at the mid-length.
  (c) Hydraulic losses concentrated at the control gate.
  (d) Neglecting effect of hydraulic losses. *Ans.* (a) 715 feet, (b) 720 feet, (c) 720 feet, (d) 740 feet.

34. Re-solve Problem 26 for an assumed pipe line head loss of 10 feet with the hydraulic losses concentrated at the discharge line outlet end. *Ans.* Head rise = 70 feet and 30 feet. Head drop = 150 feet and 100 feet.

Chapter XIV

35. Compute the maximum head at the control gate of the installation shown in Figure 95 for a uniform gate closure in 3 seconds with an initial flow of 1200 cubic feet per second. *Ans.* 630 feet.

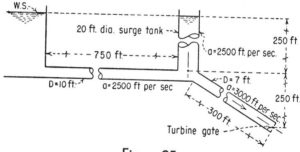

Figure 95

36. For the pipe line shown in Figure 71 of the text the control gate at *B* is initially closed. Compute the maximum head rise at *A*, *B*, and *C* when the initial flow of 150 cubic feet per section is cut off uniformly at *A* in 1.8 seconds. *Ans.* 105 feet, 80 feet, 75 feet.

Chapter XV

37. Re-solve Problem 35 by the approximate surge tank method. *Ans.* 620 feet.

38. Re-solve Problem 19 for the maximum head at the control gate by using the equivalent uniform pipe approximation. *Ans.* 675 feet.

Chapter XVI

39. Construct a gate closure time curve for the butterfly valve shown in Figure 74 of the text where the initial two-thirds of the angular closing move-

ment is performed in 10 seconds and the remaining one-third movement is accomplished in 20 seconds.

40. If the gate of Figure 23 in the text is replaced with a butterfly valve, what is the head rise at A for the flow shown for a complete closure from full gate position in 12 seconds at a uniform angular rate? *Ans.* 165 feet.

Chapter XVII

41. (a) Compute the maximum water surface elevation in the surge-tank installation shown in Figure 96 for a sudden full flow rejection of 600 cubic feet

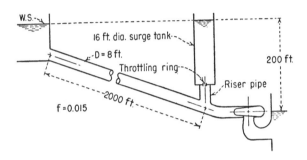

Figure 96

per second at the turbine. The surge-tank throttling ring and riser pipe loss is 40 feet for a flow of 600 cubic feet per second into or out of the surge tank.

(b) Compute the effect on the upsurge of removing the throttling effect at the surge tank. *Ans.* (a) 227 feet, (b) 242 feet.

42. Compute the downsurge in the surge tank for the installation shown in Figure 96, assuming that a pump at the lower end is delivering 600 cubic feet per second when power failure occurs. *Ans.* 50 feet.

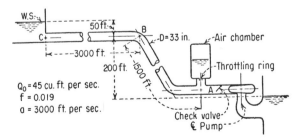

Figure 97

Chapter XVIII

43. Compute the minimum volume of an air chamber required at the pumping plant shown in Figure 97 to prevent a head rise at the pump in excess of 40 per cent of the pumping head and which does not unwater on the downsurge following a power failure at the pump motor. Use $K = 0.3$. *Ans.* 1000 cubic feet.

Index

A CATALOGUE OF SELECTED DOVER BOOKS
IN ALL FIELDS OF INTEREST

A CATALOGUE OF SELECTED DOVER
BOOKS IN ALL FIELDS OF INTEREST

CELESTIAL OBJECTS FOR COMMON TELESCOPES, T. W. Webb. The most used book in amateur astronomy: inestimable aid for locating and identifying nearly 4,000 celestial objects. Edited, updated by Margaret W. Mayall. 77 illustrations. Total of 645pp. 5⅜ x 8½.
20917-2, 20918-0 Pa., Two-vol. set $9.00

HISTORICAL STUDIES IN THE LANGUAGE OF CHEMISTRY, M. P. Crosland. The important part language has played in the development of chemistry from the symbolism of alchemy to the adoption of systematic nomenclature in 1892. ". . . wholeheartedly recommended,"—Science. 15 illustrations. 416pp. of text. 5⅝ x 8¼.
63702-6 Pa. $6.00

BURNHAM'S CELESTIAL HANDBOOK, Robert Burnham, Jr. Thorough, readable guide to the stars beyond our solar system. Exhaustive treatment, fully illustrated. Breakdown is alphabetical by constellation: Andromeda to Cetus in Vol. 1; Chamaeleon to Orion in Vol. 2; and Pavo to Vulpecula in Vol. 3. Hundreds of illustrations. Total of about 2000pp. 6⅛ x 9¼.
23567-X, 23568-8, 23673-0 Pa., Three-vol. set $27.85

THEORY OF WING SECTIONS: INCLUDING A SUMMARY OF AIR-FOIL DATA, Ira H. Abbott and A. E. von Doenhoff. Concise compilation of subatomic aerodynamic characteristics of modern NASA wing sections, plus description of theory. 350pp. of tables. 693pp. 5⅜ x 8½.
60586-8 Pa. $8.50

DE RE METALLICA, Georgius Agricola. Translated by Herbert C. Hoover and Lou H. Hoover. The famous Hoover translation of greatest treatise on technological chemistry, engineering, geology, mining of early modern times (1556). All 289 original woodcuts. 638pp. 6¾ x 11.
60006-8 Clothbd. $17.95

THE ORIGIN OF CONTINENTS AND OCEANS, Alfred Wegener. One of the most influential, most controversial books in science, the classic statement for continental drift. Full 1966 translation of Wegener's final (1929) version. 64 illustrations. 246pp. 5⅜ x 8½.   61708-4 Pa. $4.50

THE PRINCIPLES OF PSYCHOLOGY, William James. Famous long course complete, unabridged. Stream of thought, time perception, memory, experimental methods; great work decades ahead of its time. Still valid, useful; read in many classes. 94 figures. Total of 1391pp. 5⅜ x 8½.
20381-6, 20382-4 Pa., Two-vol. set $13.00

HISTORY OF BACTERIOLOGY, William Bulloch. The only comprehensive history of bacteriology from the beginnings through the 19th century. Special emphasis is given to biography-Leeuwenhoek, etc. Brief accounts of 350 bacteriologists form a separate section. No clearer, fuller study, suitable to scientists and general readers, has yet been written. 52 illustrations. 448pp. 5⅝ x 8¼.   23761-3 Pa. $6.50

THE COMPLETE NONSENSE OF EDWARD LEAR, Edward Lear. All nonsense limericks, zany alphabets, Owl and Pussycat, songs, nonsense botany, etc., illustrated by Lear. Total of 321pp. 5⅜ x 8½. (Available in U.S. only)   20167-8 Pa. $3.95

INGENIOUS MATHEMATICAL PROBLEMS AND METHODS, Louis A. Graham. Sophisticated material from Graham *Dial*, applied and pure; stresses solution methods. Logic, number theory, networks, inversions, etc. 237pp. 5⅜ x 8½.   20545-2 Pa. $4.50

BEST MATHEMATICAL PUZZLES OF SAM LOYD, edited by Martin Gardner. Bizarre, original, whimsical puzzles by America's greatest puzzler. From fabulously rare *Cyclopedia,* including famous 14-15 puzzles, the Horse of a Different Color, 115 more. Elementary math. 150 illustrations. 167pp. 5⅜ x 8½.   20498-7 Pa. $2.75

THE BASIS OF COMBINATION IN CHESS, J. du Mont. Easy-to-follow, instructive book on elements of combination play, with chapters on each piece and every powerful combination team—two knights, bishop and knight, rook and bishop, etc. 250 diagrams. 218pp. 5⅜ x 8½. (Available in U.S. only)   23644-7 Pa. $3.50

MODERN CHESS STRATEGY, Ludek Pachman. The use of the queen, the active king, exchanges, pawn play, the center, weak squares, etc. Section on rook alone worth price of the book. Stress on the moderns. Often considered the most important book on strategy. 314pp. 5⅜ x 8½.   20290-9 Pa. $4.50

LASKER'S MANUAL OF CHESS, Dr. Emanuel Lasker. Great world champion offers very thorough coverage of all aspects of chess. Combinations, position play, openings, end game, aesthetics of chess, philosophy of struggle, much more. Filled with analyzed games. 390pp. 5⅜ x 8½.   20640-8 Pa. $5.00

500 MASTER GAMES OF CHESS, S. Tartakower, J. du Mont. Vast collection of great chess games from 1798-1938, with much material nowhere else readily available. Fully annotated, arranged by opening for easier study. 664pp. 5⅜ x 8½.   23208-5 Pa. $7.50

A GUIDE TO CHESS ENDINGS, Dr. Max Euwe, David Hooper. One of the finest modern works on chess endings. Thorough analysis of the most frequently encountered endings by former world champion. 331 examples, each with diagram. 248pp. 5⅜ x 8½.   23332-4 Pa. $3.75

THE CURVES OF LIFE, Theodore A. Cook. Examination of shells, leaves, horns, human body, art, etc., in *"the* classic reference on how the golden ratio applies to spirals and helices in nature . . . . "—Martin Gardner. 426 illustrations. Total of 512pp. 5⅜ x 8½.   23701-X Pa. $5.95

AN ILLUSTRATED FLORA OF THE NORTHERN UNITED STATES AND CANADA, Nathaniel L. Britton, Addison Brown. Encyclopedic work covers 4666 species, ferns on up. Everything. Full botanical information, illustration for each. This earlier edition is preferred by many to more recent revisions. 1913 edition. Over 4000 illustrations, total of 2087pp. 6⅛ x 9¼.   22642-5, 22643-3, 22644-1 Pa., Three-vol. set $25.50

MANUAL OF THE GRASSES OF THE UNITED STATES, A. S. Hitchcock, U.S. Dept. of Agriculture. The basic study of American grasses, both indigenous and escapes, cultivated and wild. Over 1400 species. Full descriptions, information. Over 1100 maps, illustrations. Total of 1051pp. 5⅜ x 8½.   22717-0, 22718-9 Pa., Two-vol. set $15.00

THE CACTACEAE,, Nathaniel L. Britton, John N. Rose. Exhaustive, definitive. Every cactus in the world. Full botanical descriptions. Thorough statement of nomenclatures, habitat, detailed finding keys. The one book needed by every cactus enthusiast. Over 1275 illustrations. Total of 1080pp. 8 x 10¼.   21191-6, 21192-4 Clothbd., Two-vol. set $35.00

AMERICAN MEDICINAL PLANTS, Charles F. Millspaugh. Full descriptions, 180 plants covered: history; physical description; methods of preparation with all chemical constituents extracted; all claimed curative or adverse effects. 180 full-page plates. Classification table. 804pp. 6½ x 9¼.
23034-1 Pa. $12.95

A MODERN HERBAL, Margaret Grieve. Much the fullest, most exact, most useful compilation of herbal material. Gigantic alphabetical encyclopedia, from aconite to zedoary, gives botanical information, medical properties, folklore, economic uses, and much else. Indispensable to serious reader. 161 illustrations. 888pp. 6½ x 9¼. (Available in U.S. only)
22798-7, 22799-5 Pa., Two-vol. set $13.00

THE HERBAL or GENERAL HISTORY OF PLANTS, John Gerard. The 1633 edition revised and enlarged by Thomas Johnson. Containing almost 2850 plant descriptions and 2705 superb illustrations, Gerard's *Herbal* is a monumental work, the book all modern English herbals are derived from, the one herbal every serious enthusiast should have in its entirety. Original editions are worth perhaps $750. 1678pp. 8½ x 12¼.
23147-X Clothbd. $50.00

MANUAL OF THE TREES OF NORTH AMERICA, Charles S. Sargent. The basic survey of every native tree and tree-like shrub, 717 species in all. Extremely full descriptions, information on habitat, growth, locales, economics, etc. Necessary to every serious tree lover. Over 100 finding keys. 783 illustrations. Total of 986pp. 5⅜ x 8½.
20277-1, 20278-X Pa., Two-vol. set $11.00

THE ANATOMY OF THE HORSE, George Stubbs. Often considered the great masterpiece of animal anatomy. Full reproduction of 1766 edition, plus prospectus; original text and modernized text. 36 plates. Introduction by Eleanor Garvey. 121pp. 11 x 14¾. 23402-9 Pa. $6.00

BRIDGMAN'S LIFE DRAWING, George B. Bridgman. More than 500 illustrative drawings and text teach you to abstract the body into its major masses, use light and shade, proportion; as well as specific areas of anatomy, of which Bridgman is master. 192pp. 6½ x 9¼. (Available in U.S. only) 22710-3 Pa. $3.50

ART NOUVEAU DESIGNS IN COLOR, Alphonse Mucha, Maurice Verneuil, Georges Auriol. Full-color reproduction of *Combinaisons ornementales* (c. 1900) by Art Nouveau masters. Floral, animal, geometric, interlacings, swashes—borders, frames, spots—all incredibly beautiful. 60 plates, hundreds of designs. 9⅜ x 8-1/16. 22885-1 Pa. $4.00

FULL-COLOR FLORAL DESIGNS IN THE ART NOUVEAU STYLE, E. A. Seguy. 166 motifs, on 40 plates, from *Les fleurs et leurs applications decoratives* (1902): borders, circular designs, repeats, allovers, "spots." All in authentic Art Nouveau colors. 48pp. 9⅜ x 12¼.
23439-8 Pa. $5.00

A DIDEROT PICTORIAL ENCYCLOPEDIA OF TRADES AND IN-DUSTRY, edited by Charles C. Gillispie. 485 most interesting plates from the great French Encyclopedia of the 18th century show hundreds of working figures, artifacts, process, land and cityscapes; glassmaking, papermaking, metal extraction, construction, weaving, making furniture, clothing, wigs, dozens of other activities. Plates fully explained. 920pp. 9 x 12.
22284-5, 22285-3 Clothbd., Two-vol. set $40.00

HANDBOOK OF EARLY ADVERTISING ART, Clarence P. Hornung. Largest collection of copyright-free early and antique advertising art ever compiled. Over 6,000 illustrations, from Franklin's time to the 1890's for special effects, novelty. Valuable source, almost inexhaustible.
Pictorial Volume. Agriculture, the zodiac, animals, autos, birds, Christmas, fire engines, flowers, trees, musical instruments, ships, games and sports, much more. Arranged by subject matter and use. 237 plates. 288pp. 9 x 12.
20122-8 Clothbd. $14.50

Typographical Volume. Roman and Gothic faces ranging from 10 point to 300 point, "Barnum," German and Old English faces, script, logotypes, scrolls and flourishes, 1115 ornamental initials, 67 complete alphabets, more. 310 plates. 320pp. 9 x 12. 20123-6 Clothbd. $15.00

CALLIGRAPHY (CALLIGRAPHIA LATINA), J. G. Schwandner. High point of 18th-century ornamental calligraphy. Very ornate initials, scrolls, borders, cherubs, birds, lettered examples. 172pp. 9 x 13.
20475-8 Pa. $7.00

ART FORMS IN NATURE, Ernst Haeckel. Multitude of strangely beautiful natural forms: Radiolaria, Foraminifera, jellyfishes, fungi, turtles, bats, etc. All 100 plates of the 19th-century evolutionist's *Kunstformen der Natur* (1904). 100pp. 9⅜ x 12¼. 22987-4 Pa. $5.00

CHILDREN: A PICTORIAL ARCHIVE FROM NINETEENTH-CENTURY SOURCES, edited by Carol Belanger Grafton. 242 rare, copyright-free wood engravings for artists and designers. Widest such selection available. All illustrations in line. 119pp. 8⅜ x 11¼. 23694-3 Pa. $4.00

WOMEN: A PICTORIAL ARCHIVE FROM NINETEENTH-CENTURY SOURCES, edited by Jim Harter. 391 copyright-free wood engravings for artists and designers selected from rare periodicals. Most extensive such collection available. All illustrations in line. 128pp. 9 x 12. 23703-6 Pa. $4.50

ARABIC ART IN COLOR, Prisse d'Avennes. From the greatest ornamentalists of all time—50 plates in color, rarely seen outside the Near East, rich in suggestion and stimulus. Includes 4 plates on covers. 46pp. 9⅜ x 12¼. 23658-7 Pa. $6.00

AUTHENTIC ALGERIAN CARPET DESIGNS AND MOTIFS, edited by June Beveridge. Algerian carpets are world famous. Dozens of geometrical motifs are charted on grids, color-coded, for weavers, needleworkers, craftsmen, designers. 53 illustrations plus 4 in color. 48pp. 8¼ x 11. (Available in U.S. only) 23650-1 Pa. $1.75

DICTIONARY OF AMERICAN PORTRAITS, edited by Hayward and Blanche Cirker. 4000 important Americans, earliest times to 1905, mostly in clear line. Politicians, writers, soldiers, scientists, inventors, industrialists, Indians, Blacks, women, outlaws, etc. Identificatory information. 756pp. 9¼ x 12¾. 21823-6 Clothbd. $40.00

HOW THE OTHER HALF LIVES, Jacob A. Riis. Journalistic record of filth, degradation, upward drive in New York immigrant slums, shops, around 1900. New edition includes 100 original Riis photos, monuments of early photography. 233pp. 10 x 7⅞. 22012-5 Pa. $7.00

NEW YORK IN THE THIRTIES, Berenice Abbott. Noted photographer's fascinating study of city shows new buildings that have become famous and old sights that have disappeared forever. Insightful commentary. 97 photographs. 97pp. 11⅜ x 10. 22967-X Pa. $5.00

MEN AT WORK, Lewis W. Hine. Famous photographic studies of construction workers, railroad men, factory workers and coal miners. New supplement of 18 photos on Empire State building construction. New introduction by Jonathan L. Doherty. Total of 69 photos. 63pp. 8 x 10¾. 23475-4 Pa. $3.00

THE DEPRESSION YEARS AS PHOTOGRAPHED BY ARTHUR ROTH-STEIN, Arthur Rothstein. First collection devoted entirely to the work of outstanding 1930s photographer: famous dust storm photo, ragged children, unemployed, etc. 120 photographs. Captions. 119pp. 9¼ x 10¾.
23590-4 Pa. $5.00

CAMERA WORK: A PICTORIAL GUIDE, Alfred Stieglitz. All 559 illustrations and plates from the most important periodical in the history of art photography, Camera Work (1903-17). Presented four to a page, reduced in size but still clear, in strict chronological order, with complete captions. Three indexes. Glossary. Bibliography. 176pp. 8⅜ x 11¼.
23591-2 Pa. $6.95

ALVIN LANGDON COBURN, PHOTOGRAPHER, Alvin L. Coburn. Revealing autobiography by one of greatest photographers of 20th century gives insider's version of Photo-Secession, plus comments on his own work. 77 photographs by Coburn. Edited by Helmut and Alison Gernsheim. 160pp. 8⅛ x 11.
23685-4 Pa. $6.00

NEW YORK IN THE FORTIES, Andreas Feininger. 162 brilliant photographs by the well-known photographer, formerly with Life magazine, show commuters, shoppers, Times Square at night, Harlem nightclub, Lower East Side, etc. Introduction and full captions by John von Hartz. 181pp. 9¼ x 10¾.
23585-8 Pa. $6.95

GREAT NEWS PHOTOS AND THE STORIES BEHIND THEM, John Faber. Dramatic volume of 140 great news photos, 1855 through 1976, and revealing stories behind them, with both historical and technical information. Hindenburg disaster, shooting of Oswald, nomination of Jimmy Carter, etc. 160pp. 8¼ x 11.
23667-6 Pa. $5.00

THE ART OF THE CINEMATOGRAPHER, Leonard Maltin. Survey of American cinematography history and anecdotal interviews with 5 masters—Arthur Miller, Hal Mohr, Hal Rosson, Lucien Ballard, and Conrad Hall. Very large selection of behind-the-scenes production photos. 105 photographs. Filmographies. Index. Originally Behind the Camera. 144pp. 8¼ x 11.
23686-2 Pa. $5.00

DESIGNS FOR THE THREE-CORNERED HAT (LE TRICORNE), Pablo Picasso. 32 fabulously rare drawings—including 31 color illustrations of costumes and accessories—for 1919 production of famous ballet. Edited by Parmenia Migel, who has written new introduction. 48pp. 9⅜ x 12¼. (Available in U.S. only)
23709-5 Pa. $5.00

NOTES OF A FILM DIRECTOR, Sergei Eisenstein. Greatest Russian filmmaker explains montage, making of Alexander Nevsky, aesthetics; comments on self, associates, great rivals (Chaplin), similar material. 78 illustrations. 240pp. 5⅜ x 8½.
22392-2 Pa. $4.50

PRINCIPLES OF ORCHESTRATION, Nikolay Rimsky-Korsakov. Great classical orchestrator provides fundamentals of tonal resonance, progression of parts, voice and orchestra, tutti effects, much else in major document. 330pp. of musical excerpts. 489pp. 6½ x 9¼. 21266-1 Pa. $7.50

TRISTAN UND ISOLDE, Richard Wagner. Full orchestral score with complete instrumentation. Do not confuse with piano reduction. Commentary by Felix Mottl, great Wagnerian conductor and scholar. Study score. 655pp. 8⅛ x 11. 22915-7 Pa. $13.95

REQUIEM IN FULL SCORE, Giuseppe Verdi. Immensely popular with choral groups and music lovers. Republication of edition published by C. F. Peters, Leipzig, n. d. German frontmaker in English translation. Glossary. Text in Latin. Study score. 204pp. 9⅜ x 12¼.
23682-X Pa. $6.00

COMPLETE CHAMBER MUSIC FOR STRINGS, Felix Mendelssohn. All of Mendelssohn's chamber music: Octet, 2 Quintets, 6 Quartets, and Four Pieces for String Quartet. (Nothing with piano is included). Complete works edition (1874-7). Study score. 283 pp. 9⅜ x 12¼.
23679-X Pa. $7.50

POPULAR SONGS OF NINETEENTH-CENTURY AMERICA, edited by Richard Jackson. 64 most important songs: "Old Oaken Bucket," "Arkansas Traveler," "Yellow Rose of Texas," etc. Authentic original sheet music, full introduction and commentaries. 290pp. 9 x 12. 23270-0 Pa. $7.95

COLLECTED PIANO WORKS, Scott Joplin. Edited by Vera Brodsky Lawrence. Practically all of Joplin's piano works—rags, two-steps, marches, waltzes, etc., 51 works in all. Extensive introduction by Rudi Blesh. Total of 345pp. 9 x 12. 23106-2 Pa. $14.95

BASIC PRINCIPLES OF CLASSICAL BALLET, Agrippina Vaganova. Great Russian theoretician, teacher explains methods for teaching classical ballet; incorporates best from French, Italian, Russian schools. 118 illustrations. 175pp. 5⅜ x 8½. 22036-2 Pa. $2.50

CHINESE CHARACTERS, L. Wieger. Rich analysis of 2300 characters according to traditional systems into primitives. Historical-semantic analysis to phonetics (Classical Mandarin) and radicals. 820pp. 6⅛ x 9¼.
21321-8 Pa. $10.00

EGYPTIAN LANGUAGE: EASY LESSONS IN EGYPTIAN HIERO-GLYPHICS, E. A. Wallis Budge. Foremost Egyptologist offers Egyptian grammar, explanation of hieroglyphics, many reading texts, dictionary of symbols. 246pp. 5 x 7½. (Available in U.S. only)
21394-3 Clothbd. $7.50

AN ETYMOLOGICAL DICTIONARY OF MODERN ENGLISH, Ernest Weekley. Richest, fullest work, by foremost British lexicographer. Detailed word histories. Inexhaustible. Do not confuse this with Concise Etymological Dictionary, which is abridged. Total of 856pp. 6½ x 9¼.
21873-2, 21874-0 Pa., Two-vol. set $12.00

A MAYA GRAMMAR, Alfred M. Tozzer. Practical, useful English-language grammar by the Harvard anthropologist who was one of the three greatest American scholars in the area of Maya culture. Phonetics, grammatical processes, syntax, more. 301pp. 5⅜ x 8½.   23465-7 Pa. $4.00

THE JOURNAL OF HENRY D. THOREAU, edited by Bradford Torrey, F. H. Allen. Complete reprinting of 14 volumes, 1837-61, over two million words; the sourcebooks for *Walden*, etc. Definitive. All original sketches, plus 75 photographs. Introduction by Walter Harding. Total of 1804pp. 8½ x 12¼.   20312-3, 20313-1 Clothbd., Two-vol. set $70.00

CLASSIC GHOST STORIES, Charles Dickens and others. 18 wonderful stories you've wanted to reread: "The Monkey's Paw," "The House and the Brain," "The Upper Berth," "The Signalman," "Dracula's Guest," "The Tapestried Chamber," etc. Dickens, Scott, Mary Shelley, Stoker, etc. 330pp. 5⅜ x 8½.   20735-8 Pa. **$4.50**

SEVEN SCIENCE FICTION NOVELS, H. G. Wells. Full novels. *First Men in the Moon, Island of Dr. Moreau, War of the Worlds, Food of the Gods, Invisible Man, Time Machine, In the Days of the Comet.* A basic science-fiction library. 1015pp. 5⅜ x 8½. (Available in U.S. only)
20264-X Clothbd. $8.95

ARMADALE, Wilkie Collins. Third great mystery novel by the author of *The Woman in White* and *The Moonstone.* Ingeniously plotted narrative shows an exceptional command of character, incident and mood. Original magazine version with 40 illustrations. 597pp. 5⅜ x 8½.
23429-0 Pa. $6.00

MASTERS OF MYSTERY, H. Douglas Thomson. The first book in English (1931) devoted to history and aesthetics of detective story. Poe, Doyle, LeFanu, Dickens, many others, up to 1930. New introduction and notes by E. F. Bleiler. 288pp. 5⅜ x 8½. (Available in U.S. only)
23606-4 Pa. $4.00

FLATLAND, E. A. Abbott. Science-fiction classic explores life of 2-D being in 3-D world. Read also as introduction to thought about hyperspace. Introduction by Banesh Hoffmann. 16 illustrations. 103pp. 5⅜ x 8½.
20001-9 Pa. $2.00

THREE SUPERNATURAL NOVELS OF THE VICTORIAN PERIOD, edited, with an introduction, by E. F. Bleiler. Reprinted complete and unabridged, three great classics of the supernatural: *The Haunted Hotel* by Wilkie Collins, *The Haunted House at Latchford* by Mrs. J. H. Riddell, and *The Lost Stradivarius* by J. Meade Falkner. 325pp. 5⅜ x 8½.
22571-2 Pa. $4.00

AYESHA: THE RETURN OF "SHE," H. Rider Haggard. Virtuoso sequel featuring the great mythic creation, Ayesha, in an adventure that is fully as good as the first book, *She.* Original magazine version, with 47 original illustrations by Maurice Greiffenhagen. 189pp. 6½ x 9¼.
23649-8 Pa. $3.50

UNCLE SILAS, J. Sheridan LeFanu. Victorian Gothic mystery novel, considered by many best of period, even better than Collins or Dickens. Wonderful psychological terror. Introduction by Frederick Shroyer. 436pp. 5⅜ x 8½.   21715-9 Pa. $6.00

JURGEN, James Branch Cabell. The great erotic fantasy of the 1920's that delighted thousands, shocked thousands more. Full final text, Lane edition with 13 plates by Frank Pape. 346pp. 5⅜ x 8½.
                                                                23507-6 Pa. $4.50

THE CLAVERINGS, Anthony Trollope. Major novel, chronicling aspects of British Victorian society, personalities. Reprint of Cornhill serialization, 16 plates by M. Edwards; first reprint of full text. Introduction by Norman Donaldson. 412pp. 5⅜ x 8½.   23464-9 Pa. $5.00

KEPT IN THE DARK, Anthony Trollope. Unusual short novel about Victorian morality and abnormal psychology by the great English author. Probably the first American publication. Frontispiece by Sir John Millais. 92pp. 6½ x 9¼.   23609-9 Pa. $2.50

RALPH THE HEIR, Anthony Trollope. Forgotten tale of illegitimacy, inheritance. Master novel of Trollope's later years. Victorian country estates, clubs, Parliament, fox hunting, world of fully realized characters. Reprint of 1871 edition. 12 illustrations by F. A. Faser. 434pp. of text. 5⅜ x 8½.   23642-0 Pa. $5.00

YEKL and THE IMPORTED BRIDEGROOM AND OTHER STORIES OF THE NEW YORK GHETTO, Abraham Cahan. Film *Hester Street* based on *Yekl* (1896). Novel, other stories among first about Jewish immigrants of N.Y.'s East Side. Highly praised by W. D. Howells—Cahan "a new star of realism." New introduction by Bernard G. Richards. 240pp. 5⅜ x 8½.   22427-9 Pa. $3.50

THE HIGH PLACE, James Branch Cabell. Great fantasy writer's enchanting comedy of disenchantment set in 18th-century France. Considered by some critics to be even better than his famous *Jurgen*. 10 illustrations and numerous vignettes by noted fantasy artist Frank C. Pape. 320pp. 5⅜ x 8½.   23670-6 Pa. $4.00

ALICE'S ADVENTURES UNDER GROUND, Lewis Carroll. Facsimile of ms. Carroll gave Alice Liddell in 1864. Different in many ways from final Alice. Handlettered, illustrated by Carroll. Introduction by Martin Gardner. 128pp. 5⅜ x 8½.   21482-6 Pa. $2.50

FAVORITE ANDREW LANG FAIRY TALE BOOKS IN MANY COLORS, Andrew Lang. The four Lang favorites in a boxed set—the complete *Red, Green, Yellow* and *Blue* Fairy Books. 164 stories; 439 illustrations by Lancelot Speed, Henry Ford and G. P. Jacomb Hood. Total of about 1500pp. 5⅜ x 8½.   23407-X Boxed set, Pa. $15.95

HOUSEHOLD STORIES BY THE BROTHERS GRIMM. All the great Grimm stories: "Rumpelstiltskin," "Snow White," "Hansel and Gretel," etc., with 114 illustrations by Walter Crane. 269pp. 5⅜ x 8½.
21080-4 Pa. $3.50

SLEEPING BEAUTY, illustrated by Arthur Rackham. Perhaps the fullest, most delightful version ever, told by C. S. Evans. Rackham's best work. 49 illustrations. 110pp. 7⅞ x 10¾. 22756-1 Pa. $2.50

AMERICAN FAIRY TALES, L. Frank Baum. Young cowboy lassoes Father Time; dummy in Mr. Floman's department store window comes to life; and 10 other fairy tales. 41 illustrations by N. P. Hall, Harry Kennedy, Ike Morgan, and Ralph Gardner. 209pp. 5⅜ x 8½. 23643-9 Pa. $3.00

THE WONDERFUL WIZARD OF OZ, L. Frank Baum. Facsimile in full color of America's finest children's classic. Introduction by Martin Gardner. 143 illustrations by W. W. Denslow. 267pp. 5⅜ x 8½.
20691-2 Pa. $3.50

THE TALE OF PETER RABBIT, Beatrix Potter. The inimitable Peter's terrifying adventure in Mr. McGregor's garden, with all 27 wonderful, full-color Potter illustrations. 55pp. 4¼ x 5½. (Available in U.S. only)
22827-4 Pa. $1.25

THE STORY OF KING ARTHUR AND HIS KNIGHTS, Howard Pyle. Finest children's version of life of King Arthur. 48 illustrations by Pyle. 131pp. 6⅛ x 9¼. 21445-1 Pa. $4.95

CARUSO'S CARICATURES, Enrico Caruso. Great tenor's remarkable caricatures of self, fellow musicians, composers, others. Toscanini, Puccini, Farrar, etc. Impish, cutting, insightful. 473 illustrations. Preface by M. Sisca. 217pp. 8⅜ x 11¼. 23528-9 Pa. $6.95

PERSONAL NARRATIVE OF A PILGRIMAGE TO ALMADINAH AND MECCAH, Richard Burton. Great travel classic by remarkably colorful personality. Burton, disguised as a Moroccan, visited sacred shrines of Islam, narrowly escaping death. Wonderful observations of Islamic life, customs, personalities. 47 illustrations. Total of 959pp. 5⅜ x 8½.
21217-3, 21218-1 Pa., Two-vol. set $12.00

INCIDENTS OF TRAVEL IN YUCATAN, John L. Stephens. Classic (1843) exploration of jungles of Yucatan, looking for evidences of Maya civilization. Travel adventures, Mexican and Indian culture, etc. Total of 669pp. 5⅜ x 8½. 20926-1, 20927-X Pa., Two-vol. set $7.90

AMERICAN LITERARY AUTOGRAPHS FROM WASHINGTON IRVING TO HENRY JAMES, Herbert Cahoon, et al. Letters, poems, manuscripts of Hawthorne, Thoreau, Twain, Alcott, Whitman, 67 other prominent American authors. Reproductions, full transcripts and commentary. Plus checklist of all American Literary Autographs in The Pierpont Morgan Library. Printed on exceptionally high-quality paper. 136 illustrations. 212pp. 9⅛ x 12¼. 23548-3 Pa. $12.50

AN AUTOBIOGRAPHY, Margaret Sanger. Exciting personal account of hard-fought battle for woman's right to birth control, against prejudice, church, law. Foremost feminist document. 504pp. 5⅜ x 8½.
20470-7 Pa. $5.50

MY BONDAGE AND MY FREEDOM, Frederick Douglass. Born as a slave, Douglass became outspoken force in antislavery movement. The best of Douglass's autobiographies. Graphic description of slave life. Introduction by P. Foner. 464pp. 5⅜ x 8½. 22457-0 Pa. $5.50

LIVING MY LIFE, Emma Goldman. Candid, no holds barred account by foremost American anarchist: her own life, anarchist movement, famous contemporaries, ideas and their impact. Struggles and confrontations in America, plus deportation to U.S.S.R. Shocking inside account of persecution of anarchists under Lenin. 13 plates. Total of 944pp. 5⅜ x 8½.
22543-7, 22544-5 Pa., Two-vol. set $12.00

LETTERS AND NOTES ON THE MANNERS, CUSTOMS AND CONDITIONS OF THE NORTH AMERICAN INDIANS, George Catlin. Classic account of life among Plains Indians: ceremonies, hunt, warfare, etc. Dover edition reproduces for first time all original paintings. 312 plates. 572pp. of text. 6⅛ x 9¼. 22118-0, 22119-9 Pa.. Two-vol. set $12.00

THE MAYA AND THEIR NEIGHBORS, edited by Clarence L. Hay, others. Synoptic view of Maya civilization in broadest sense, together with Northern, Southern neighbors. Integrates much background, valuable detail not elsewhere. Prepared by greatest scholars: Kroeber, Morley, Thompson, Spinden, Vaillant, many others. Sometimes called Tozzer Memorial Volume. 60 illustrations, linguistic map. 634pp. 5⅜ x 8½.
23510-6 Pa. $10.00

HANDBOOK OF THE INDIANS OF CALIFORNIA, A. L. Kroeber. Foremost American anthropologist offers complete ethnographic study of each group. Monumental classic. 459 illustrations, maps. 995pp. 5⅜ x 8½.
23368-5 Pa. $13.00

SHAKTI AND SHAKTA, Arthur Avalon. First book to give clear, cohesive analysis of Shakta doctrine, Shakta ritual and Kundalini Shakti (yoga). Important work by one of world's foremost students of Shaktic and Tantric thought. 732pp. 5⅜ x 8½. (Available in U.S. only)
23645-5 Pa. $7.95

AN INTRODUCTION TO THE STUDY OF THE MAYA HIEROGLYPHS, Syvanus Griswold Morley. Classic study by one of the truly great figures in hieroglyph research. Still the best introduction for the student for reading Maya hieroglyphs. New introduction by J. Eric S. Thompson. 117 illustrations. 284pp. 5⅜ x 8½. 23108-9 Pa. $4.00

A STUDY OF MAYA ART, Herbert J. Spinden. Landmark classic interprets Maya symbolism, estimates styles, covers ceramics, architecture, murals, stone carvings as artforms. Still a basic book in area. New introduction by J. Eric Thompson. Over 750 illustrations. 341pp. 8⅜ x 11¼.
21235-1 Pa. $6.95

AMERICAN ANTIQUE FURNITURE, Edgar G. Miller, Jr. The basic coverage of all American furniture before 1840: chapters per item chronologically cover all types of furniture, with more than 2100 photos. Total of 1106pp. 7⅞ x 10¾.　21599-7, 21600-4 Pa., Two-vol. set $17.90

ILLUSTRATED GUIDE TO SHAKER FURNITURE, Robert Meader. Director, Shaker Museum, Old Chatham, presents up-to-date coverage of all furniture and appurtenances, with much on local styles not available elsewhere. 235 photos. 146pp. 9 x 12.　22819-3 Pa. $6.00

ORIENTAL RUGS, ANTIQUE AND MODERN, Walter A. Hawley. Persia, Turkey, Caucasus, Central Asia, China, other traditions. Best general survey of all aspects: styles and periods, manufacture, uses, symbols and their interpretation, and identification. 96 illustrations, 11 in color. 320pp. 6⅛ x 9¼.　22366-3 Pa. $6.95

CHINESE POTTERY AND PORCELAIN, R. L. Hobson. Detailed descriptions and analyses by former Keeper of the Department of Oriental Antiquities and Ethnography at the British Museum. Covers hundreds of pieces from primitive times to 1915. Still the standard text for most periods. 136 plates, 40 in full color. Total of 750pp. 5⅜ x 8½.
23253-0 Pa. $10.00

THE WARES OF THE MING DYNASTY, R. L. Hobson. Foremost scholar examines and illustrates many varieties of Ming (1368-1644). Famous blue and white, polychrome, lesser-known styles and shapes. 117 illustrations, 9 full color, of outstanding pieces. Total of 263pp. 6⅛ x 9¼. (Available in U.S. only)　23652-8 Pa. $6.00

Prices subject to change without notice.

Available at your book dealer or write for free catalogue to Dept. GI, Dover Publications, Inc., 31 East Second Street, Mineola, N.Y. 11501. Dover publishes more than 175 books each year on science, elementary and advanced mathematics, biology, music, art, literary history, social sciences and other areas.